Psychomotor Aspects of Mental Disease

PSYCHOMOTOR ASPECTS OF MENTAL DISEASE

An Experimental Study

By H. E. KING, *Ph.D.*

Associate Professor of Psychiatry
(Research Psychology)
Tulane University School of Medicine

PUBLISHED FOR
THE COMMONWEALTH FUND

Harvard University Press, Cambridge, Massachusetts
1954

LIBRARY OF CONGRESS CATALOG CARD NO. 54–8526

PRINTED IN THE UNITED STATES OF AMERICA

Published for
The Commonwealth Fund
By Harvard University Press
Cambridge, Massachusetts

For approximately a quarter of a century THE COMMONWEALTH FUND, through its Division of Publications, sponsored, edited, produced, and distributed books and pamphlets germane to its purposes and operations as a philanthropic foundation. On July 1, 1951, the Fund entered into an arrangement by which HARVARD UNIVERSITY PRESS became the publisher of Commonwealth Fund books, assuming responsibility for their production and distribution. The Fund continues to sponsor and edit its books, and co-operates with the Press in all phases of manufacture and distribution.

Distributed in Great Britain
By Geoffrey Cumberlege
Oxford University Press, London

TO THE SUBJECTS WHO TOOK PART
IN THIS EXPERIMENT

ACKNOWLEDGMENTS

ASSISTANCE of many different kinds was required to complete these studies, and it is a pleasure to acknowledge the contribution of several institutions and individuals to the work.

The patients studied were drawn from the following institutions: Greystone Park State Hospital, New Jersey, Dr. Archie Crandell, Medical Superintendent and Chief Executive Officer; The New York State Psychiatric Institute, Dr. Nolan D. C. Lewis, Director; and the Tulane University School of Medicine, New Orleans, Out-Patient Psychiatric Clinic, Dr. Robert G. Heath, Director. The active cooperation of the administration and personnel of each of these institutions made it possible to study patient groups with well-documented individual clinical histories.

The non-patients who gave of their time to participate as subjects in this study are too numerous to list individually, but the author wishes to take this opportunity to acknowledge the invaluable contribution of such cooperation wherever given.

Dr. Carney Landis, Principal Research Psychologist of the New York State Psychiatric Institute, and Johs. Clausen, Mag. Art., Associate Research Scientist, New York State Psychiatric Institute, who served as advisors at many steps along the way, also read the manuscript in preparation and offered many helpful suggestions for the presentation of material. The writer is indebted also to Dr. Joseph Zubin, R. E. Corrigan and Leona Bersadsky for technical assistance; and to Don Alvarado for the preparation of all drawings and figures.

The author, in addition, is deeply grateful to all those who have assisted in the task of preparing this monograph for the press.

In particular I have valued the support of Dr. R. G. Heath, Chairman, Department of Psychiatry and Neurology, Tulane University School of Medicine.

Finally, and principally, I should like to acknowledge the constant counsel of my wife, Dr. Kathleen Young, Tulane University School of Medicine, who, more than any other, lent aid to these studies from start to completion.

H. E. K.

New Orleans, La.
May, 1954

CONTENTS

FIGURES

TABLES

PART I

Problems and Methods

CHAPTER 1

INTRODUCTION AND FORMULATION OF THE PROBLEM

THE study of certain psychomotor aspects of mental disease to be reported in the present experiment is based, in the broadest sense, on the notion that the power of animate organisms to move is their most striking characteristic and serves an important function in all of the adaptive activities of human and animal life. The capability of spontaneous and rapid motor response to stimulation, internal and external, forms the most basic distinction of animal life from other forms of living matter. All animals, from the most primitive forms to man, share this response characteristic and exhibit its operation in their adjustment to the world about them. The evolution of the animal orders demonstrates that an increasing degree of control is exercised over responsive movements in association with the development of more complex nervous structures, permitting a wider range and increased subtlety of responsive behavior. All animals, however, continue to exhibit motor responsiveness as their principal form of adaptation to the immediate environment. In man, the unique development of mind makes possible "trial activity" in the form of conscious thought, and the direct tie between stimulus and motor response is lessened, so that we cannot always adequately infer the stimulus to action by observing the response made. Even in man, however, movement continues to play a major role in the adjustment of the individual to his circumstances, whether consciously directed by thought, or more unconsciously determined by automatic and learned responses. We have before us much to learn of the way in which man's mental abilities exercise control over his behavior, but the study of his responsive movements remains a primary source of information about him, whatever the prominence of mental activity, in the form of conscious thought, in his behavior.

In the study of behavior disorder, one of the principal stumbling blocks which has retarded experimental progress in understanding the nature of the disorder is the fact that we have been unable to apply many of our scientific techniques to the problem at hand. Despite obvious deviation from the normal in the behavior and mental content of the patient with a behavior disorder, there are no identifiable disturbances at the somatic level. The newcomer to the field thinks that surely the gross impairments of mind and behavior so plainly visible in so many cases must of necessity have reflections in the physical or physiologic make-up of the individual. When he begins to look into the matter, however, he finds an astonishingly small amount of evidence of an interference with normal bodily processes which might be either causally related to the mental disturbance or even a direct reflection of the disordered mental state. Although various irregularities of body function may occur inconsistently, there is no physical or physiologic test in use today which serves to identify the presence of mental disease, much less indicates the severity of disorder. The definition and diagnosis of mental disease continue to rest upon the clinical history of the individual and the record of his actions. On the psychologic side the situation is but little more promising. One might expect to find that clear, measurable psychologic parallels exist which either account for or accompany a condition of behavior disorder, but there has been great difficulty in demonstrating this experimentally. The identification of the mentally ill person, or the estimation of the extent of a mental disorder, has proved to be little assisted by psychologic test methods as compared with the opinion formed on the basis of knowledge of the behavior of the patient and of his life history. These comments on our inability to isolate physical and psychologic concomitants of the behavior disorders should not be considered to be a resignation to the fact that no relationships exist or to belittle what evidence we have been able, by dint of strenuous effort, to place on record. Rather, they state that we have been most consistently thwarted in our efforts to acquire sufficient basic data on patients suffering from mental complaints to be able to begin the piecing together of systematic theories as to what is structurally involved in behavior disorder or even what psychologic elements are concerned, and in what manner.

The view that movement factors play a primary role in the adaptation of all animate life forms to the environment has led us to postulate that a careful study of the characteristics of movement response among subjects suffering with a behavior disorder might provide us with an index of the faulty adaptive processes characteristic of mental disease. This impression has been strengthened by a review of clinical observations made on patients with a behavior disorder, and, more specifically, by several objective observations made in the course of study of the effects of the removal of prefrontal gray matter on brain function and psychotic symptomatology.

In an attempt to register the psychologic effects of removal of cortical tissue from the human frontal lobes, the psychologists of the Columbia-Greystone Associates, of whom the author was one, applied a large and varied battery of psychologic tests to a group of mentally ill patients selected to undergo psychosurgery (topectomy) for the relief of mental symptoms (26). This broad test battery included measures of intellectual function, learning and retention, the ability to abstract, memory and associative processes, time judgment, affective processes, and so on. These same tests were repeated at specified times after operation with the intention of registering defects or alterations of psychologic process associated with the loss of brain tissue, its locale, and the amount of tissue destruction. The single most striking result of this work was the general absence of defect, either physical or psychologic, which accompanied known damage to the frontal cortex. These patients had not received a detailed psychomotor evaluation but had given performance on many tasks including a psychomotor component, such as the Porteus Maze Test or the Continuous Problem Test. Scores on such tests indicated that even before coming to operation the psychomotor performance of the mental patients of this group was of a faulty and retarded nature. A second group studied was given a more direct psychomotor appraisal, and, although the group was relatively small, several observations made on its performance seemed to indicate that psychomotor measurement methods might usefully serve as an indication of the degree of behavior disorder present (68, 69). As had been noted with the first group, preoperative psychomotor performance was found to be somewhat retarded and appeared to be particularly defective when contrasted with performance on non-psychomotor tasks.

There seemed to be little doubt that the individuals under study were, for one reason or another, alike in exhibiting defective performance on psychomotor tests, despite rather wide deviations in their clinical appearance. A comparison with the data of a small normal group examined with the same test battery served to emphasize further this difference, for the deviation of the psychotic group from normal on non-psychomotor tests was minimal compared with performance on the psychomotor tests included. It was also noted that although the various non-psychomotor tests had failed to reflect any change in the status of the patients after frontal cortical surgery, the psychomotor tests, and tasks including a major psychomotor component, regularly demonstrated a further impairment during the immediate postoperative period, at which time such operative procedures produce a temporary exacerbation of psychotic symptoms (44). It appeared, on the basis of such trends in the data, that tasks with a psychomotor element were sensitive to the presence of psychosis and seemed to be appropriately modified by changes in clinical status. The data available furnished only a very rough indication that the foregoing statement is correct in any general sense, for the clinical estimates were subjectively made and the test methods employed were less than perfect; but they did seem to furnish sufficient evidence to warrant further inquiry on a more systematic basis. It is the purpose of the experiments contained in this report to examine, by means of more exact methods of observation, the possibility of demonstrating a relationship between psychomotor performance and behavior disorder.

A review of the literature showed that much the same sort of psychomotor defects had been noted among psychotic cases since Kraepelin first set up his diagnostic categories. Scattered through the writings of the past half century there are to be found any number of observations which point more or less directly to the presence of such an impairment in psychosis. These vary from rather general observations on the bizarre posturing of some individual patient to systematic surveys of large mental hospital populations with one or another type of observation or measurement. The most informative of these are the experiments of Huston, Shakow, et al., who conducted investigations of motor functions in schizophrenia, observing reaction time, tapping speed, steadiness, and work rates (49, 50, 52, 122, 123). These workers, reviewing what had been known before and adding their own important observations, made it clear that such phenomena do indeed exist among schizophrenic and manic-depressive patients, and attributed them to the lowered motivational status of these patients.

It appears, then, that the psychomotor component is of direct interest in the study of psychosis and that it has been found to be so many times. If this is true, however, why is it not more actively pursued and experimented upon? Lacking, as we do, any method other than the clinical by which we may measure the presence or severity of mental disorder, it is surprising to find that any method which achieves this goal, or even approximates it, is not in widespread use both clinically and in research. It is always difficult, if not impossible, to answer questions of this kind as to why some things command scientific attention while others do not. Perhaps it is not important whether they can be accounted for as long as practical use may be made of neglected findings in shaping the course of contemporary investigation. Several different forces probably have combined to obscure the potential value of psychomotor observation of the mentally ill. One is the limited nature of many of the observations, resembling more closely the specific details of behavior for a given patient or small group of patients than anything which possesses generality. Another is perhaps owing to the time factor in historical development. Psychomotor studies were an early interest of experimental psychologists, and studies of reaction time and other measures of timed psychomotor response had a great vogue in the infancy of psychology, accompanied by many efforts to relate such measures to other psychologic functions of the individual. Two deterrent influences were soon encountered; first, the demonstration that different types of psychomotor performance are quite specific and exhibit rather low intercorrelations, and second, the fact that such measures exhibit very low correlations with psychometric intelligence. The rise of the mental testing movement at the turn of the century rather stole the limelight and, in addition, made it clear that measures of an individual's speed and quality of motor response were of little assistance in predicting his success at intellectual tasks, such as success in school, etc. The Binet movement, as is well known, was actually an effort to cease attempting to understand the individual by an atomistic approach and to employ more global concepts of reaction, such as judgment, reasoning, etc. The fact that psychomotor tests did not correlate very well with intelligence measures presently resulted in their omission from mental tests and their relegation to a position of peripheral value —similar to that occupied by measures of sensory activity—in understanding the mental life. This was true, at least, of the evaluation of intelligence, the factor which at the time dominated thinking about the psychology of the individual.

In recent years the focus of attention in psychology has shifted to the attempt to understand factors in the personality and emotional life of the individual, as well as the purely intellectual side. The rise of systems of psychodynamics in psychiatry paralleled the extension of interest by psychologists to other than intellectual abilities of the individual and helped to place stress on the influences impinging on the growth and existence of the individual and the formative effect of such influences on the development of personality. A more or less direct product of this attitude, along experimental and diagnostic lines, has been the recent interest in the study of perception, of how the individual receives his experience and is interactive with the stimulus world about him. An attention to response capacities, such as the psychomotor, while in no sense opposed to this interest, has in general played a much lesser role. Even those current methods of appraising the individual which include a psychomotor component lay great stress on the perceptual and thought-organizational elements of the behavior observed.

There is no conflict of interests here, of course; the above comment is intended only to indicate that attention has largely centered recently on the perceptual processes in our experimental and diagnostic thinking. A re-examination of the interrelations between psychomotor response capacities and the life patterns of the individual seems due, if not overdue, to round out the picture and to bring its comparisons with other aspects of the individual up to date with regard to more recent concepts of mental life. One cannot, of course, in any given study undertake the compilation of all known facts and data pertaining to animate motion; this is a task for many men representing all the varied disciplines of biologic science, but one may be guided by the continued importance of motor behavior in the life of man, however covered over by complex mechanisms, to single out movement as a basic approach in attempting to understand more fully various aspects of man's more complicated behavior patterns. The quest, in the broadest sense, is to determine just how the factor of movement relates to all of the other things we know about the individual: to emotion, intelligence, stress, expression, personality, mood, and so on. These broad questions, however, cannot all be investigated simultaneously. As a beginning, the two potentially most productive areas for study appear to be a concentration on the observable phenomena associated with mental disease, and investigation in areas also involving neurophysiology, where the details of neurologic alterations of status, principally of brain structure and physiology, may be known. Investigations following these twin lines of inquiry are under way in our laboratories at the moment. The present report is concerned only with some of the phenomena observable in mental disease, together with some more general comments and speculation on the subject of animate movement. Other investigations of psychomotor responses centering about experimental variations of neurologic structures and physiology have been given, in part, in conjunction with the report of the other disciplines concerned (62, 64, 68, 69, 70); still others are in progress.

The immediate task, then, is to select from the vast repertoire of possible psychomotor movements what appear to be representative movements, in the sense that they sample many related types of actions; to apply these to defined experimental groups with behavior disorder; and to compare the responses obtained. It will be necessary to know how non-psychotic subjects perform these tasks and how the different tasks interrelate among normal subjects. We must examine closely the effects of practice and evaluate the variability as well as the mean level of performance in the non-psychotic group. All of these same factors may then be examined in groups of psychopathologic patients, arranged in a sequence from most to least disturbed, to determine the possible presence of defect, its extent if present, the interrelations among the measures, acquisition, correlation with various validating criteria, and so on. The two chapters to follow will describe the methods and groups employed in the present experiment to obtain answers to these questions, and the remainder of the report will present the findings and their possible interpretation in the light of related information from the work of other investigators.

CHAPTER 2

SELECTION AND DESCRIPTION OF THE TEST BATTERY

THE difficulties of measuring behavior patterns of any sort are too well known to require repetition here. Even the simplest modes of activity, such as the feeding or sleeping habits of laboratory animals, demand special methods of observation and often the use of complicated registering systems in order to record what has taken place. More complex behavior, particularly the sort of activities characteristically human, present infinitely greater problems of observation and notation to the investigator. Most such activities cannot, for a variety of reasons, be observed with anything approaching completeness, and we must rely on sample measures as representative of the more general life activity of the individual. As Scott has pointed out, the description of an object of complex physical shape is in itself complex if the entire object is to be described. The shape of a tooth, for example, would require an extremely complicated geometric description to be complete. We may, however, simplify the problem and render a workable approximation of the object by indicating a few key measurements, e.g., type, height, length, width, etc., or by the construction of an approximate diagram embodying such measures. So, too, with behavior we attempt to convey some idea of its real dimensions by the description of what are thought to be key measurements of the important factors. The adequacy of the approximation thus depends altogether on the importance and accuracy of the measures employed, for the presence of error in key measurements results in a defeat of their original purpose.

It is never a simple matter to single out the important elements of behavior in any of its varieties, and psychomotor behavior is no exception to the general rule. The infinitely great number of movements made by man resist any simple classification as to type, and the answer to the question of what constitutes the key or important measures of psychomotor behavior is far from simple by reason of the extraordinary complexity of movement phenomena. The same is true, in fact, of most psychologic activities which we arbitrarily classify as functions. The measurement of intellectual abilities, to take our most intensively studied material by way of example, has proceeded upon empirical grounds, beginning with observations on maturation and gradually extending its correlations to other criteria. Even at present, after years of study and practice in measuring intellectual ability, we find it difficult to specify its major dimensions. The observation of correlation clusters and the method of factor analysis have helped point the way, but we have only begun to sort out the principal elements involved. For similar reasons, i.e., the diffuseness and complexity of the expression of the characteristic, we have scarcely begun to identify the key factors in psychomotor response. The initial approach must be empirical, therefore, making observations on the characteristic at work with the hope that common trends or elements will become more clearly visible when our knowledge of such facts has become more extensive.

The primary attitude we must abandon is that all externally visible movements possess some demonstrably common core, are positively interrelated and exhibit a kinship in performance. This is no more true or in keeping with the known facts than would be a statement that all mental abilities are so related, but it is an error much more commonly made. Stated more positively, this means that psychomotor behavior is an entire realm of human activity in itself, exhibiting varied characteristics, which is to be studied as such, and that a framework must be outlined to describe its major dimensions or ways of expression. We have examined portions of this structure by observing here something about athletic ability and there something about manual dexterity or work methods and so on. Each of these ways of making observations is but a part, an important one but only a part, of a broad range of psychomotor activities, and any comprehension we may gain about the range as a whole must depend upon information gathered from many and varied levels of psychomotor expression. The term *intelligence* has served as a description of the whole field of intelligent behavior and intellectual ability and has furnished a constant reminder that a broad range of activities, rather than a single element, was being discussed. A similar term, such as *psychomotility,* may serve to remind us that an entire range of activities of the psychomotor sort may be grouped for purposes of discussion and yet include varied types of action.[1]

From the more general category of psychomotor action two major subdivisions have been made by investigators working in this field: (1) *gross movement patterns,* referring to the more or less general bodily activities, e.g., spontaneous movement, athletics, dancing, movements during sleep, etc.; and (2) *fine movement patterns,* referring to the coordinations of smaller musculatures (usually of the extremities) where strength is secondary to speed or precision or both, e.g., handling tiny objects, typing, reaction time, etc. This distinction of type of movement coordinations has been proved a valuable one, the recognition of which aids in the selection of appropriate investigative methods for the problem at hand. It should be noted that the term *fine* does not imply tiny or minimal movements, but is intended to specify those motor coordinations "in which the factor of strength is secondary to speed or precision, or both" (118). Experimental studies of both fine and gross movement patterns among psychopathologic subjects are needed. The recent work of Kinder (60, 61) in applying the time-sampling method of behavior study to the activity of psychotic patients is a most important contribution to our knowledge of the relation of psychopathology to gross movement patterns and the influence of frontal brain damage upon this relationship. The present study will concentrate on the fine movement patterns of psychopathologic patients, observing several types of such movement. Aided by the division of psychomotor activities into the above

[1] The fact that a low degree of relationship exists between measures of different sorts of psychomotor activity is well known to workers in the field of motor skills, mechanical aptitudes, etc., and has been recently summarized by Seashore (118). The above restatement of principles derived from experimentation with normal individuals and their performance on a variety of psychomotor tasks is intended to serve as a reminder to those whose primary interest is behavior pathology that we must guard against oversimplification of what, on close inspection, proves to be a decidedly complex system in the normal individual.

dichotomy the problem of selecting key measures for investigating the influence of psychopathology on psychomotor abilities is somewhat simplified. By restricting this investigation to the observation of fine motor coordinations exclusively we may concentrate our effort on this portion of the total range of possible human psychomotor activities.

To know which of the measures of fine psychomotor ability may best serve as samples of this type of activity we may make use of the results of factor analyses of performance by normal individuals on a variety of fine psychomotor tasks. One of the uses of this method of analysis is to reduce a large set of descriptive phenomena to a smaller set, or number of factors, which in skeleton form best represent the original structure of descriptive phenomena. In simpler words, it may be used to select, at least approximately, a few tests from a series which are the essence of the larger series from which they were drawn. Such analyses have been made of the intercorrelations obtained from normal performance on a variety of fine psychomotor tests and have pointed to the possible existence of several major elements running through such performance. In an unpublished study the author found three essential factors in an analysis of fourteen tests of fine psychomotor ability which are in reasonable agreement with three of the six factors (Factors I, II, and IV) reported by Seashore, Buxton, and McCullom to characterize their factor analysis of twenty-one instrumental motor tests, undertaken for a similar purpose (119).[1] These common factors have been employed as the best available guide to the types of fine psychomotor performance it would appear most profitable to investigate around the variable of psychopathology. The three tests which are most closely identified with these three common factors have been selected as the key tests in the formation of the test battery of this study.

Factor I was tentatively identified as the speed of initiating movement. This is similar to Factor I of Seashore, Buxton, and McCullom, identified as the "speed of single reaction."

Factor II was tentatively identified as the speed of stereotyped

[1] It is interesting to note that these are essentially the same factors which had previously been found to characterize a wide variety of psychomotor tasks employed in industrial selection, although these tasks were often also loaded by the element of spatial perception (64, 68, 69).

wrist-arm movement. This is similar to Factor II of Seashore, Buxton, and McCullom, identified as "finger, hand and forearm speed in restricted oscillatory movement."

Factor III was tentatively identified as manual and finger dexterity. This is similar to Factor IV of Seashore, Buxton, and McCullom, identified as "precision."

Accepting these as a guide for the investigation of comparative performance by psychopathologic groups, three tasks were selected, one for each of the above factors, to be administered to selected groups of mental patients so that their relative performance might be observed. It should be stressed that these are not presented as the ultimate, best or most fruitful types of fine psychomotor ability to observe, but were the methods of choice in terms of currently available information.

To be of value in the consideration of the speed and adequacy of psychomotor response these procedures must seek to remove, so far as possible, any ambiguity as to the role of the subject. They must be extremely simple and as free as possible from demands upon the intelligence and language facility of the subject. The tasks must be thoroughly understood and well practiced and stabilized before sample measures are made for inclusion in group comparisons. The need for considerable practice at each task prior to taking the test measure is essential for several reasons. For one, it insures the subject's understanding of just what he is to do and how he is to do it. This permits him to become familiar with the procedure and the examiner and is likely to give him an opportunity to relax more in the test situation. When many subjects are studied, coming from all manner of previous backgrounds, the allowance of practice should help to reduce the initial advantages which might be possessed by those more familiar with fine motor performance by reason of their life history. This last does not assume the importance one might at first suppose, for it has been demonstrated that prior experience with what appear to be very similar actions has little actual effect on such test measures (93, 118, 135, 140), but the allowance of practice trials with the specific task may act as an extra safeguard in this respect. Most important of all, however, are two final factors. A long practice series, the results of which are fully recorded, gives us the opportunity to observe the acquisition of the response and establish a learning curve which is essential in interpreting the data obtained after the responses have become stabilized. In addition, as Garrett has pointed out for psychologic measures generally, the allowance of practice tends to bring out individual differences more strongly (38), making for more adequate measurement of both the individual and the group. As a consequence of one or all of these factors, the allowance of practice produces a more stable and reliable and less variable measure.

THE TEST BATTERY

Speed of initiating single movements

The most representative test of Factor I, the speed of initiating single movements, appears to be a measure of simple reaction time. Two measures of simple hand reaction time have been employed throughout this study to obtain sample measures of the speed of initiating single movements in response to auditory signals. The first is of the sort classically employed in laboratories of psychology for this measurement and requires the subject to lift his right forefinger from a resting point or key in response to an auditory signal. The second is also a familiar type of measurement, usually referred to as "jump reaction time," in which the subject must move his finger through a short distance and press a key in response to an auditory signal (65). Both of these responses were made to auditory stimuli, rather than the more usual visual signals, in the belief that an auditory stimulus would be more attention-compelling and better suited to use with psychopathologic subjects.

An apparatus was constructed which would make it possible to obtain both of these measures by a single reaction on the part of the subject. He is seated at a table so that his responding member has freedom of action and is requested to place his right index finger on a rest situated on a test board immediately in front of him. He is then instructed that, immediately upon hearing an auditory signal sounded (e.g., a buzzer), he is to lift his finger, cross the board, and depress a telegraph key 10.5 in. distant (see diagram in Figure 3). A "ready" signal always preceded the sounding of the stimulus, varying in a random fashion from 1 to 4 seconds before stimulation. The apparatus was so designed (see Appendix C for details) that upon closing the circuit for the presentation of the stimulus two chronoscopes were activated: one was stopped (by means of a resistance relay) the instant the subject's finger left the rest, and the other by the subject's pressing of the telegraph key. The fast component, or lifting of the finger from the rest, constitutes the measure of lift reaction time and was read from a chronoscope graduated in milliseconds; the slow component, or cross-and-press response, constitutes the measure of jump reaction time and was read from a chronoscope graduated in hundredths of a second. The subject was unaware that this stratification of his response was being made, and his set was for cross-and-press response. This arrangement has the added benefit of "catching" any premature response, since the lift reaction time chronoscope will remain at zero if the finger is prematurely off the rest (i.e., prior to the sounding of the stimulus).

The stimulus signal was clear, with a sound value of 55.0 decibels measured at the distance of the average ear, 30 in. away. The telegraph key tension was set such that 230 gm. of weight were required for a complete closure. Time delays in the activation of the various elements in the system were determined by cathode ray oscilloscope, and the necessary corrections have been made to the chronoscope readings.

Responses were performed with the right hand throughout, since experience has revealed that the actual preference, in terms of performance, for the left hand is shown by but a small percentage of the total population, although subjective preference and ambidexterity are commonly reported. Twenty practice trials were performed and another 20 trials served as the test measure for each of the indicators, lift reaction time and jump reaction time. The subject was not permitted knowledge of his scores while being tested.

The mental set for the subject who is set to cross-and-press as a response is different from the more usual lift-instantly mental set employed in classical reaction time studies. This would be a constant for all subjects in the present experiment, however, and need not disturb comparative studies. A group of subjects with a lift-instantly set have been tested with the same apparatus, and their data will be given in the section on results with normal sub-

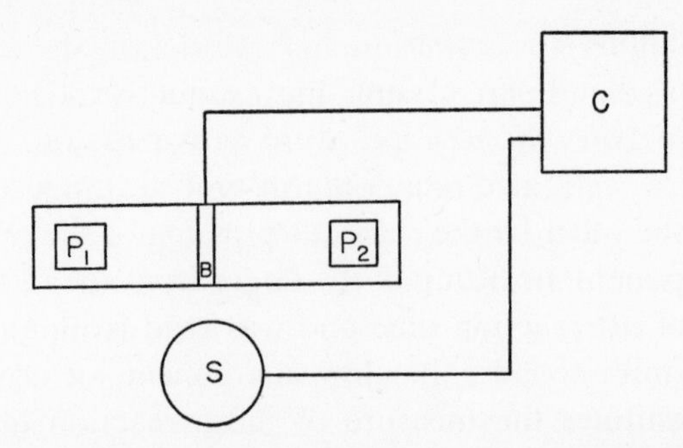

FIGURE 1. Diagram of the tapping test apparatus. *P*, metal plates 2 x 2 in. square, mounted at a distance of 12 in. between inner edges; *B*, barrier raised 1/2 in. above base; *S*, subject; *C*, time control and kymograph. (See Appendix C for wiring diagram.)

jects, so that a comparison of these two measures may be made to make it possible to compare these data with the values given in other studies.

For simplicity of reference in text and tabular matter the measure of simple hand lift reaction time to an auditory stimulus will be referred to by the symbol *RT* (*L*), and the measure of simple hand jump reaction time to an auditory stimulus will be indicated by the symbol *RT* (*J*). When these tests are discussed in the text to follow as measures of reaction time, it should be borne in mind that they are more specifically measures of reaction time of a certain type, that described above, and do not imply that reaction time is a general bodily category of response.

Speed of tapping

The best single test of the second factor, "finger, hand and forearm speed in restricted oscillatory movement," appears to be the speed of tapping in a horizontal plane. Measures of this function were made in the manner familiar in psychologic laboratories, with some minor modification (66).

An apparatus was constructed which allowed each individual tap in a 5-second interval to be recorded automatically. Figure 1 diagrammatically shows the test situation.

The subject is seated facing the board so that his right arm, bent at the elbow, is suspended above the midpoint or barrier. He is instructed to place his right index finger on the barrier and at the starting signal to begin tapping alternately between the two metal plates as rapidly as possible until signaled to stop. The placement of the midline barrier requires an arc of movement to be used between the two plates. The apparatus was so designed that touching the plates with the finger was sufficient to activate a resistance relay which would trigger the recording system. This does away with the usual metal stylus and attached wire required for completing an electrical circuit and permits a very natural movement of the fingers and hand, obviating the difficulties so often met by ways of grasping a stylus, plate oxidation, etc.

Tapping was recorded in 5-second intervals with "ready," "go," and "stop" signals given by voice. The actual period of time for the measure was, however, governed by an electronic interval timer which operated within this period to give exact delimitation of the test interval. Each tap was recorded by an ink-pen on a moving strip of kymograph paper, together with the actual beginning and end of the test interval. This method of recording permits a total count for the entire test interval, and also makes it possible to analyze subdivisions of the total test period, acceleration rates, etc.

Responses were made with the right hand throughout. Fifteen practice trials were performed by each subject and another 10 trials served as the test measure for the indicator of speed of tapping, *Tap*. The subject was not given knowledge of the recorded information about his performance while being tested, but could, of course, witness his own performance. During the practice series the subject was allowed to rest for approximately 3 seconds after each test interval and for 15 seconds after each 5 trials. A rest period of 1 minute separated the practice series from the test series. During the test series approximately 3 seconds' rest was allowed between test intervals and 15 seconds' rest after 5 test trials, midway in the series.

Finger dexterity

The most representative test of the third factor, "manual and finger dexterity" or "precision," appears to be the dexterity and speed with which small objects are handled by the fingers on a pegboard. Measures of this function were made, using the Purdue Pegboard, a commercially available test of dexterity developed primarily for use in industrial selection. Figure 2 diagrams the test situation.

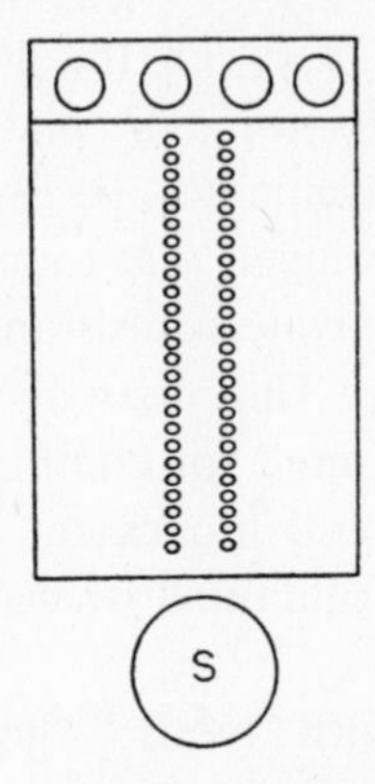

FIGURE 2. Diagram of the dexterity test (the Purdue Pegboard). A wooden board 12 x 17 1/2 inches with supply boxes at the top to hold pins, washers, and collars, and a double row of 25 holes down the center for the insertion of pins. *S*, subject (132).

In this test the subject is required to handle small metal objects with the right and left hand individually and with both hands used together. He is first instructed[1] to begin to pick up pins, one at a time, from a supply box at the top of the board and insert them in a row of holes extending the length of the board. "Ready," "start," and "stop" signals are given by voice and the time interval for performance is determined by a fast stopwatch. He is then instructed to accomplish a similar task with the left hand, and then using the two hands simultaneously. A time interval of 30 seconds is set for each of these tasks. One further sequence, performed with the two hands simultaneously, requires more minute finger movements in the assembly of pins, small washers, and collars into a specified pattern of peg, washer, collar, washer, using the hands alternately for the placing of pieces in the assembly. As both hands are used at all times in an alternating fashion, this permits anticipation of the next element to be added to the assembly. One minute is allowed for the construction of as many of these assemblies as possible. Scores are as follows:

Right hand (*R*): Number of pins placed with the right hand in 30 seconds.

Left hand (*L*): Number of pins placed with the left hand in 30 seconds.

Both hands (*B*): Number of pairs of pins placed in 30 seconds.

[1] A more detailed listing of the instructions used with this test may be found in the report by its authors, J. Tiffin and E. J. Asher, The Purdue Pegboard: Norms and studies of reliability and validity. *J. Appl. Psychol.*, 1948, *32*, 234–247.

Right plus left plus both hands (*RLB*): A composite score which is the total of the three foregoing.

Assembly (*Assem*): Number of parts assembled in 1 minute.

Each subject performed 2 practice trials at each task, and a third trial served as the test measure. All 3 trials were completed before moving on to the next task, an arrangement which permits some transfer effect. The subject was allowed approximately 20 seconds' rest between trials, plus whatever time the instructions occupied between the different tasks, a minimum of 45 seconds. Testing was always begun with the right hand. The subject was not given his scores while being tested, but, of course, could witness his own performance. All of the scores listed above were recorded, but only the composite measure of right and left and both hands (*RLB*) and the assembly (*Assem*) score will be given in the tables, to represent dexterity. These are the principal scores, and since the *RLB* score is actually a composite made up of performance by the right and left hands separately it includes all the performance given.

These are the primary measures included, most nearly representing the major factors thought to exist in fine psychomotor movements. In addition to these primary measures, it was desired to add a task of elementary disjunctive reaction or discrimination response. The major reason for this inclusion was an interest in the factor of "elementary decision" or discrimination on the first factor of reaction time. A second, and perhaps equally important, reason for its inclusion was to aid in maintaining interest in the reaction time task while getting the large number of practice trials needed. This additional measure, though not of a kind with the three preceding, has been employed throughout all groups tested.

Disjunctive lift reaction time

A simple disjunctive lift reaction time was measured as it is usually done in psychologic laboratories and employed the apparatus previously described for simple reaction time. The subject is required to cross-and-press a telegraph key placed 10.5 in. distant and to the right in response to an auditory signal, a buzzer. Figure 3 shows diagrammatically this relative position. After a series of

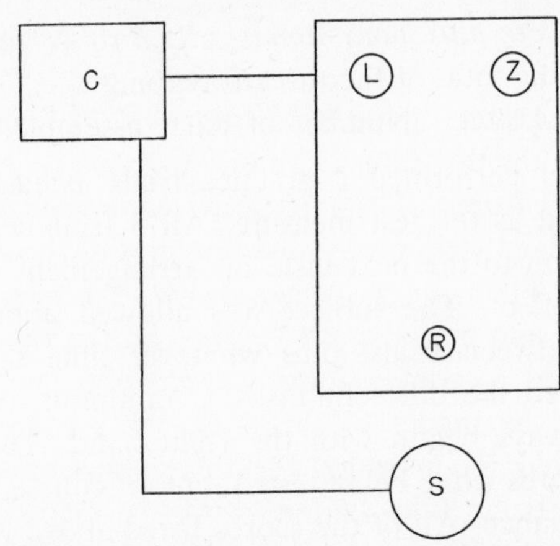

FIGURE 3. Diagram of the reaction time apparatus. *R*, rest; *Z*, response key to buzzer; *L*, response key to bell; *S*, subject; *C*, stimulus control and chronographs. (See Appendix C for wiring diagram.)

5 practice responses to this stimulus he is instructed to make a similar response, using the same hand, to the key placed an equal distance away and to the left when a bell is sounded. After 5 practice trials to this key in response to the bell he is again asked to respond to the buzzer by pressing the key on the right for 5 trials and finally 5 more trials in response to the bell. This gives a total of 20 responses, 10 to the right key in response to a buzzer and 10 to the left key in response to a bell. The subject is then asked to make a discrimination; that is, to listen and identify the type of signal sounded and to make the appropriate response by pressing the key on the right if the buzzer is sounded (the same key always used with the buzzer) or pressing the key on the left if the bell is sounded (the same key always used with the bell). A series of 10 trials involving this choice is made, using a predetermined order of stimuli chosen by random numbers (see Appendix C for the order).

All of the preceding constitute the practice or learning series. An equal number of test trials are run, after a 20-minute rest period, repeating the entire sequence, which serves as the indicator of disjunctive lift reaction time, *DRT* (*L*). One half of the subjects were started by being given the buzzer as the first signal to which they would respond, and one half were started with the bell. "Ready" signals were always given just as they were described for simple reaction time. The time required for response was recorded in milliseconds.

The procedure for obtaining disjunctive lift reaction time was interwoven with the measures of simple reaction time in the following manner: Measures of the response to a signal in which no choice was involved were always the first part of the task performed by the subject. The sequence was always a buzzer-and-right-key half of the time and bell-and-left-key half of the time, always with full instruction as to which signal was coming and to which key response should be made. In this way, the simple reaction time situation prepared the way for the discrimination to follow, the subject by then being fully familiar with the response required to each of the stimuli. When beginning the test series the simple situation again always preceded the discrimination situation. As mentioned above, this procedure serves to add variety to the subject's task and helps considerably in maintaining interest through the long series of responses required. Because the discrimination measures follow the simple in the practice series, this much additional practice at the task is also obtained before beginning the test trials. Adding all responses given, simple and disjunctive, each subject has 30 practice trials before the test measure proper is begun.

Pilot experimentation was undertaken with this task to determine whether simple reaction time to the two different stimuli was actually of a similar order. The sound values of the stimuli were equated (55 db.), and the data from the pilot group indicated no difference in timed response to the different stimulus signals. This factor will also be analyzed in the larger test groups which follow.

Disjunctive jump reaction time

This measure is similar in every way to that described for *DRT* (*L*), for it is a portion of the same series of responses. The *RT* (*J*) is actually the slower component, the time required to cross-and-press, of the simple reaction time situation, and, of course, the disjunctive jump reaction time, *DRT* (*J*), is the same, slower component of the disjunctive responses described in the preceding section. The time required for response was recorded in hundredths of a second.

As may readily be observed, several of these tasks, *RT* (*L*),

RT (*J*), *DRT* (*L*), and *DRT* (*J*), all center about one principal process, that of initiating a single response to a prearranged signal. As such, they may be expected to show high intercorrelations and a good many similarities. Even so, there appears sufficient reason to warrant their separate observation, at least in this early phase of investigation. Actually, the *RT* (*L*) is the fundamental measurement, the time lapse between stimulus reception and the execution of a simple effector movement. *RT* (*J*), while very similar, extends this situation somewhat by including the identical sensory components, but requiring the completion of a more complex response movement. We know from experimental evidence (138) that the required movement, in a measure of this kind, is but the visible component of a complex response actually involving considerably more musculature, but that the musculature involved in making a response is of considerably less importance in its determination than is the pattern of movement employed. This situation, dividing the same response into the two fractions of *RT* (*L*) and *RT* (*J*), although probably exhibiting a higher correlation than would jump reaction time and lift reaction time generally, serves to augment the essential measurement by requiring an extended movement, the thrust across 10.5 in. to the response key. We have, in a sense, an index of the time of first beginning a response movement, and an opportunity to observe further variations in recruitment which may occur in making a thrust movement. In the same way, the introduction of a discrimination situation is a complication which may be expected to extend observations on the reaction time process to situations involving elementary complexity and some degree of judgment.

Table 1 summarizes the information about each of the tests in the experimental battery, providing a central, brief statement of what is measured by each, the procedure, and the nature of the score obtained.

Summarizing briefly, also, the reasons for selecting this particular battery of tests for experimental use with groups of psychopathologic patients, several major considerations have governed this choice. Of the numerous aspects of psychomotility it is possible to observe, fine motor movements are the most easily isolated from other quali-

TABLE 1. Tests in the experimental battery

Test	Abbreviation	Nature	NO. OF TRIALS Practice	NO. OF TRIALS Measure	Units of score	Direction of score
Reaction time (lift)	*RT (L)*	Time lapse between stimulus onset and simple effector lifting movement to remove finger from start point	20	20	Milliseconds	Time score; smaller score means faster performance
Reaction time (jump)	*RT (J)*	Time lapse between stimulus onset and completion of cross-and-press effector movement to press telegraph key 10.5″ distant	20	20	Hundredths of a second	Time score; smaller score means faster performance
Tapping speed	*Tap*	Maximal no. of finger taps which can be made alternating between two metal plates, 12″ apart, in a 5 sec. interval	15	10	No. of taps	Unit score; larger score means faster performance
Dexterity-Precision: Sum of performance by right, left, & both hands used together	*RLB*	Maximal no. of metal pegs which can be inserted in a row of holes in 30 sec. with right hand, no. inserted with left hand in 30 sec., & no. of pairs of peg insertions made in 30 sec., all added together	2 (each task)	1	No. of pegs properly placed	Unit score; larger score means faster performance

(*continued on page 26*)

TABLE 1. Tests in the experimental battery (*continued*)

Test	Abbreviation	Nature	NO. OF TRIALS		Units of score	Direction of score
			Practice	*Measure*		
Assembly	*Assem*	Maximal no. of assemblies of 4 small metal parts, each successive piece added by alternate hand in 60 sec.	2	1	No. of parts properly assembled	Unit score; larger score means faster performance
Disjunctive reaction time (lift)	*DRT (L)*	Time lapse between stimulus onset and completion of effector lifting movement to remove finger from start point when discrimination of total response must be made to press one key if buzzer sounds, another if bell sounds	10	10	Milliseconds	Time score; smaller score means faster performance
Disjunctive reaction time (jump)	*DRT (J)*	Time lapse between stimulus onset and completion of cross-and-press effector movement when discrimination of response must be made to press one key if buzzer sounded, another if bell sounded	10	10	Hundredths of a second	Time score; smaller score means faster performance

ties of the organism. They are easily comprehended by the subject and are largely free of known connections with intelligence, previous life history, work habits of the individual, and so on. They may be highly repetitive without being exhaustive in time or effort and thus may permit detailed observation of their acquisition. They possess a common factor of speed of mobilization and appear basic, in the sense of being indivisible, and, speaking more speculatively, probably have the most direct connection to the neural substratum of any of the voluntary activities.

CHAPTER 3

EXPERIMENTAL GROUPS AND PROCEDURE

THE proper test for the existence of the postulated defect in fine motor abilities among the mentally ill consists of contrasting the performance records of a group of individuals with unmistakable mental disorder with that of a group in which no mental disturbances have been identified. To extend the hypothesis somewhat further, it is useful also to determine the level of fine psychomotor ability of several groups of patients who are mentally disordered, graded in terms of the severity of their mental disturbance, so that any relation which obtains between the severity of the disease process and the degree of fine psychomotor impairment may become apparent. The experimental design of the present study was organized around these two principles.

A clear understanding of the performance of the normal, or non-pathologic, group is of fundamental importance in making any comparisons, for it establishes the base line, or performance that may be expected. All of the tasks which make up the present test battery are familiar ones to those acquainted with psychologic methods, and comparisons of the data gathered from psychopathologic patients might conceivably be made by using only what is known of normal performance from the accumulated experience of many investigators (93, 118, 140). A particular effort has been made, however, to include data from normal groups in this study itself for several reasons. Foremost is the fact that the details of procedure, apparatus, and instructions usually exert some influence on the data obtained, and thus the best comparisons with pathologic material may be made where identical test methods are followed for both normal and experimental groups. A study of normal performance with the specific battery of tests selected also permits the necessary comparison of performance among the various tests, since the several tests have been administered to a common population. One of the questions which calls for an experimental answer is whether the interrelation among the fine psychomotor abilities is affected by the presence of mental disorder, and by establishing the degree of correlations existing in the performance of normal subjects on the experimental test battery, a point for this comparison is established. A further reason for the inclusion of data from the normal is based on the need for adequate practice at the tasks and observation of the usual course of learning. For reasons given in the preceding chapter, this is of special importance in interpreting the data obtained in the test measures proper. By considering first the performance of normal persons on the identical test battery we can best demonstrate and review all of the usual factors encountered in such performance and form a clear idea of what constitutes expected performance, with which the data of the psychopathologic groups are to be compared.

PILOT EXPERIMENTATION

The experimental test battery was first used with several small groups of normal subjects, prior to undertaking the extensive collection of data, in order to work out the most profitable procedures to follow. This type of experimentation serves as a guide only and does not, of course, yield final answers to questions of procedure. The primary aim of this work was to establish what appeared to be the number of practice and test measures required to achieve a reasonable degree of stability.

Reaction time (lift)

Twenty practice trials were found adequate to permit stabilization of this measure, approximating the final level achieved after considerably longer practice. On this task, as well as the others, the level of performance achieved after 20 trials does not represent the very last possible achievement of the subject at his physiologic limit, but definitely approximates it at what Woodworth has called the "good enough" level, referring to the terminal level of a practice curve. Prolonged practice with a few subjects indicated that most of the improvement consequent upon repeated practice takes place in the first 20 trials, with very little further gain after many repetitions, a finding which is in agreement with the reports of several investigators (93, 140).

It was determined that a separation of the practice series from the trial series by a rest of 20 minutes enhanced continued interest in the task, and that this period was equally beneficial whether filled with actual rest or a change to performance on a different task. Consequently the procedure used was to obtain the *RT* (*L*) practice trials at the beginning of the examination, followed by the tapping test and dexterity measures and then a return to the *RT* (*L*) task for the additional 20 trials which served as the test measure.

Reaction time (jump)

This measure is closely associated with *RT* (*L*) and was found to follow much the same course. Twenty practice trials were found to be sufficient to produce an asymptotic level of the learning curve. As this measure is directly linked with *RT* (*L*), the identical rest sequence applies.

Tapping speed

Fifteen practice trials, with rest periods of 3 seconds between trials, 15 seconds after every 5 trials and 1 minute between practice and test series, were found sufficient to achieve stabilization on the tapping task, yielding a level very close to that achieved after extended practice. The rest periods were determined so as to provide sufficient rest for the most energetic tappers, since presumably the amount of fatigue would be directly related to the rate of work.

Dexterity

Following the instructions of the authors of the Purdue Pegboard Test, 3 trials were given on each subtest before passing on to the next. The pilot group data showed that very definite gains in performance could be seen from one trial to the next for these 3 trials. When the subjects were given additional practice, the learning curves rapidly flattened and stabilized at the level reached on the fourth trial, which was slightly above that reached on trial 3. The level reached with 3-trial administration seems to give a reasonable approximation of final level, and, since conservation of testing time was an added factor, it was decided that this would provide a serviceable measure. In situations where testing time is not an important factor it would probably be best to allow somewhat more practice at the dexterity tasks to achieve further stabilization.

NORMAL GROUP

Use of the term *normal* immediately raises the question of what constitutes normality. As employed in this study, it refers to a group of individuals who have shown no clear signs of mental disturbance, who are not hospitalized for any cause whatever, who are working members of the community, and for whom no indication of erratic behavior is known to their employers. Although these restrictions may be expected to eliminate the markedly deviant cases, it may be anticipated that some few mentally deviant individuals may meet such criteria successfully, but no detailed attempt has been made to detect them or remove them from the series. Since the principal aim of the study is to contrast the fine psychomotor performance of those with clear-cut psychopathology with that of normal individuals, any unintentional inclusion of unstable cases into the normal sample will tend to lessen the contrast, rather than to accentuate it. The examiner's appraisal of the subject at the time of securing data does not, of course, represent a detailed psychiatric inquiry, but each individual reported in this study was personally examined by the author and no individuals with major mental disturbance were found to be present.

Age and sex are sample characteristics which would be expected to exert some influence on the data obtained from the fine psychomotor performance of normal subjects. It seems clear from the reports of previous investigations that other characteristics, such as race, I.Q., socio-economic levels, etc., are not related factors and would not be expected to act as controlling elements in selection (93, 118, 135, 140). As an added safeguard in the selection of normal subjects, an effort has been made to achieve maximum heterogeneity in the sample with regard to occupation, years of schooling, socio-economic level, and I.Q. All records in both normal and psychopathologic groups were drawn from a single race, white. The normal group is made up of professional workers, building maintenance crews, secretarial and clerical workers, businessmen and women, and a varied series composed of neighbors and relatives of these persons.

Age and sex, as has been noted, are important determining factors of fine psychomotor ability, and require special attention in the design of experiments. It is well known that aging exerts an influence on most psychomotor functions, including the fine psychomotor abilities, and that it does so differentially for individuals and for specific tasks (93). As a rule, the psychomotor abilities of the individual gradually increase through childhood, achieving a maximum at about age 20, and remain at approximately this level without major deterioration until about age 70, after which a decline may be noted. In view of these facts, the age range covered by this sample was set between 20 and 70 years to extend over the long period between reaching psychomotor maturity and eventual decline. The extension over so wide an age range results in a large number of subjects in the total sample, since there must be a sufficiently large number in each age decade if we are to have an adequate basis for comparison.

As the principal comparisons intended are with groups of mental patients whose general age characteristics are known (79), the normal sample was selected with this in mind. Although subjects between the ages of 20 and 70 are included, the age range in which the mental diseases with which we are concerned occur most frequently was emphasized. That is to say, more subjects were included in the age range of 20 to 50 years than of the later years, since this is the age range in which most schizophrenias and neuroses occur (79). The normal sample studied includes 194 subjects; Table 2 gives the distribution of the total sample by age decade.

It is known that sex differences exist on fine psychomotor performance of this type, but that these differences are usually slight. In order to neutralize this factor in the comparison group of normal persons an effort was made to compose the group of an equal number of male and female subjects in each age decade. The practical difficulties of obtaining subjects resulted in a slight favoring of male subjects in the total sample, 104 males to 90 females, with some irregularities in the distribution at each age decade but not

TABLE 2. Age and sex distribution of the normal group

Age group, years	*Males*	*Females*	*Total*
20–29	24	20	44
30–39	33	22	55
40–49	23	21	44
50–59	12	14	26
60–69	12	13	25
TOTAL	104	90	194

Average age: males 41.4 years
females 43.1 years
total 42.2 years

Age range of total sample 20.7–69.4 years

so great as to introduce a strong bias factor. Table 2 shows the distribution of subjects for the total normal group by age and sex. They are approximately evenly distributed in the various age decades, the exception being largely in the 30- to 39-year group. The actual age range of the normal subjects is 20.7 to 69.4 years, and the average ages of male and female groups approximate one another.

CHRONIC SCHIZOPHRENES

For psychopathologic material of the most disordered kind, patients suffering from schizophrenia have been selected in this study. Landis has well summarized the opinion of most in saying, "Dementia Praecox is the most disabling of all varieties of mental illness; it lasts longer, has fewer recoveries, and is the most difficult for the patient, his relatives and his friends to understand" (77).

The group of patients on whom psychomotor observations have been made will be referred to as the chronic schizophrenic group. It is made up of 90 patients (45 male, 45 female) committed to mental institutions, with a median duration of 9.1 years' hospitalization with this diagnosis. The series includes no patient who has not been committed to a mental hospital for at least 1 year. The behavior disorder of these patients may be said to be both chronic and severe; chronic because of its long history, and severe enough to require isolation from society by commitment to a mental institution. Beyond this criterion of severity, however, such a group is obviously made up of cases with varying degrees of behavior disturbance; at least, this is so at any given moment. They may be classified into rough subgroups on the basis of the degree to which their behavior is disordered by the disease process, as this may best be judged by criteria which go beyond the diagnosis or the fact of commitment. Three methods of ordering the chronic group along these lines have been employed, each used to divide the total group into three subdivisions of the most disturbed, moderately disturbed, and least disturbed patients. It must be borne in mind that these gradations come only after the initial criterion of diagnosis and commitment, and that even the relatively least disturbed subgroup still exhibits clear deviation from the norm.

Gradation by psychiatric scale

In 1947 Malamud and Sands published a revised psychiatric rating scale, the purpose of which was to make it possible to represent numerically the degree to which the behavior of a given patient deviated from his prepsychotic norm (85). The scale consists of 19 items which refer to observable elements in the behavior of the patient:

1. Appearance
2. Motor activity
3. Responsivity
4. Aggressiveness
5. Socialization
6. Attention
7. Speech
8. Nutrition
9. Sexuality
10. Sleep
11. Work
12. Mood
13. Affect
14. Feeling
15. Awareness
16. Associations
17. Content
18. Memory
19. Thought processes

Each item is anchored on a 12-point continuum, extending in two directions from a midpoint of normal behavior. Deviations to one side represent symptoms directed away from the person, and to the other side those directed internally (for the complete scale, see Appendix B). The items are divided into those elements of behavior which can be directly observed at the time of the interview, those which rest upon observation of ward behavior, and those which can be evaluated only on the basis of verbal communication with the patient. This method of representing quantitatively the behavior of psychotic patients has been found by the authors to possess reasonable validity and a high degree of reliability in the hands of different raters. Although the scale was specifically designed to compare the behavior of a given patient with his own prepsychotic level, it has also been found to be of value in comparing the clinical course of one patient with that of another (96).[1]

The Malamud-Sands scale has been employed in this experiment, not for the purpose of plotting the clinical course of a given patient, but as one method of classifying the degree to which psychotic symptoms are expressed in the chronic group. Each patient of the series was interviewed by an independent examiner, who conducted an extensive mental examination, and inquired at length into the patient's problems, hospital adjustment, plans for the future, and so on. On the basis of the information elicited during this interview, each patient was rated on the psychiatric scale. The only modification made in the use of the scale which represents a departure from the use prescribed by its authors was an extension of the time period during which specific observations are made of ward activities. Four of the functions depend upon continuous observation by ward personnel for their adequate evaluation, and, since the scale was devised to reflect clinical alterations in the course of therapy, the period of ward observation was relatively brief, 24 hours. This period has been extended to 7 days in the present study, as the patients were not in the course of therapy and it was felt that the longer time period provided better material upon which to base judgment.

The scale yields a single score, a total of the deviations from the prepsychotic norm on each of the 19 items described above, weighting each at 1. Higher numerical scores reflect a markedly disturbed condition; lower scores indicate a lesser departure from previous normality. The psychiatric scale scores of the chronic group

[1] Since this experiment was begun, further revisions of the Psychiatric Rating Scale have been published by S. L. Sands and W. Malamud (A rating scale analysis of the clinical effects of lobotomy. *Am. J. Psychiat.*, 1949, *105*, 760–766) and by J. Hope, F. Elmadjian, and W. Malamud (A method for the evaluation of hormone therapy in schizophrenia. *J. clin. & exp. Psychopath.*, 1951, *12*, 267–282).

were then placed in rank order, and the group was divided into three subgroups containing equal numbers of subjects. These are called the most disturbed, moderately disturbed, and least disturbed subgroups. The division into groups of equal number is somewhat arbitrary and was intended simply to divide the upper, lower, and middle groups of a ranked series.

Gradation by psychologic scale

King et al. have emphasized the value of making detailed observations on the behavior exhibited by subjects while performing psychologic tests, with particular reference to the value of such observations among those with chronic mental illness (70). Ratings of this kind do not refer to how well or poorly the subject is doing on the tests proper, but attempt to focus on elements in the approach and behavior of the subjects in the test situation. The psychologic examiner always strives to make the test situation as similar and as standard as possible from one subject to another in order to render the test performance of different subjects directly comparable. This also provides an opportunity to throw into relief the differences in behavior of different subjects as they approach the same task. These authors have devised a scale composed of 14 items representing observable and non-overlapping characteristics of behavior which can be rated at the time of taking psychologic tests. The items are:

1. Cooperation
2. Relevant verbalization
3. Apparent memory
4. Expressive play
5. Grasp of instructions
6. Effort on test
7. Willingness
8. Attention to test
9. Self-criticism
10. Self-confidence
11. Rapport
12. Intrusion of psychotic influence
13. Confusion
14. Personal concern with the examiner

Each of these characteristics is represented on a graphic scale along a continuum ranging from zero expression to normal or overexpression. Definitions of each category or item are before the rater at all times, and each item is anchored at five points along the continuum (for the complete scale see Appendix B). This method of representing quantitatively the behavior of psychotic patients at the time of taking psychologic tests has also been found to possess reasonable validity and a high degree of reliability between raters. When ratings are made after observing performance on very different types of tasks (e.g., projective and psychomotor tests) inter-rater reliability is understandably somewhat lower ($r = .71$), but when the tasks are of approximately the same type (e.g., aphasia or memory examination and intelligence tests) inter-rater correlations range from .87 to .93. The scale, as originally devised, was intended for use in plotting the course of therapy, and two of the items, *apparent memory* and *confusion,* are inapplicable in the present context and have been omitted.

The King et al. scale has been employed in this experiment, like the psychiatric scale previously described, as another method of classifying the degree to which psychotic aberrations of behavior were observable in the chronic group at the time of psychomotor testing. The total scale yields a single score, which is the sum of deviations from the norm on 12 of the 14 items of the original scale, weighting each at 1. Low numerical scores on this scale reflect markedly disturbed behavior at the time of psychomotor testing, and high scores indicate a lesser departure from normality. These total scores were placed in rank order and the total group was divided into three numerically equal subgroups: most disturbed, moderately disturbed, and least disturbed patients.

Gradation by management criteria

The way in which hospital authorities are required to care for their patient population furnishes a rough indication of the degree of behavior disturbance expressed. Some patients must be under constant individual supervision; others can be handled in groups; still others may be given a large measure of responsibility for their own management. In this experiment the total group of chronic patients has been classified according to their status as determined by the hospital authorities charged with their care. Three categories have been established:

1. Patients kept on disturbed wards.
2. Patients kept on locked wards.
3. Patients who live in wards but who are working about the hospital.

TABLE 3. Age and sex distribution of the chronic group

Age group, years	Males	Females	Total
10–19	3	0	3
20–29	9	5	14
30–39	11	13	24
40–49	11	10	21
50–59	6	13	19
60–69	5	4	9
TOTAL	45	45	90

Average age: males 40.8 years
females 44.9 years
total 42.9 years

Age range, total 17.4–68.8 years

The chronic group has been classified by these standards into three unequal groups: 8 from disturbed wards, 58 from locked wards, and 24 who are ward patients but also work about the hospital.

These three methods of establishing subgroups in the chronic group are to be regarded as supplementary, differentiating the degrees of severity of disorder beyond the initial criterion of diagnosis, commitment, and isolation from society. In addition to this major classification the case history of each patient was abstracted systematically to make it possible to treat the data gathered by psychomotor methods in terms of such factors as age, sex, health, educational level, body type, duration of illness, type of psychopathology, etc. (The outline followed in the recording of these data may be found in Appendix A.)

The age range of the chronic group is from 17.4 to 68.8 years; the sex composition is equal for the total group, 45 males and 45 females. The age and sex composition by decades is given in Table 3. The mean age for the chronic group very closely approximates that of the normal sample: 42.2 years for the normal group and 42.9 years for the chronic group. The age ranges are also in good approximation, though extending somewhat lower in the age scale for the chronic group.

It was not certain, at the outset of data collection, to what extent cooperation in the test situation would play a role in obtaining records. Prior experience had indicated that this type of measure may be made in a remarkably large proportion of mental patients and this proved to be true for the present series. Actually, 100 patients were selected from various wards of a large hospital (treating 5,000 patients) and brought in for interview and testing. Of these, only 10 were not amenable to testing by reason of strong withdrawal, fear, or anger; therefore the series was not subject to strong selection by this factor.

The rating of behavior on the psychologic scale was always made at the end of the testing session, while the patient was still present. Immediately thereafter the patient was given an interview by the independent examiner which served as the basis for the psychiatric behavior scaling.

SUBACUTE BEHAVIOR DISORDERS

We are lacking a term to describe that broad category of individuals who show definite signs of a disordered mental life, with specific symptoms and usually a diagnosis, but whose difficulty is not so severe as to require commitment and isolation in a mental hospital. These may, at least for purposes of discussion in this experiment, be thought of as subacute disorders, in the sense that although some disorder is clearly present, it is not sufficiently acute to require commitment to an institution. This group, which will be referred to as the subacute group, is made up of individuals whose symptoms lead to a diagnosis of pseudoneurotic schizophrenia or neurosis.

Hoch and Polatin have recently pointed out that both the qualitative and quantitative aspects of symptom expression must be taken into account in the diagnosis of mental disorder, and have distinguished a large group of patients with a neurotic-like disorder which they hold to be a pseudoneurotic expression of schizophrenia (47).[1] Patients so diagnosed are similar in many ways to patients usually diagnosed as neurotics, and an adequate distinction between these diagnoses rests upon extensive information about the patient

[1] These authors say, in the summary of their article, "Attention is called to a group of patients who show a clinical symptomatology which is considered by many psychiatrists to be psychoneurotic. These patients do not deteriorate and have no delusions or hallucinations. Nevertheless, they show clinical symptomatology which is very similar to that seen in schizophrenic patients. It can be demonstrated in follow-up studies that a considerable number of these patients have short psychotic episodes or later become frankly schizophrenic. A few of these

(*continued on page 40*)

and his psychodynamics. At the present time it is instructive to consider the performance of neurotic and pseudoneurotic individuals in two different ways:

1. As a single group in which there is a behavioral abnormality of sufficient clarity to distinguish it from the normal, yet not so severe as to require commitment and isolation in an institution.
2. As two separate subgroups of neurosis and pseudoneurotic schizophrenia, diagnosed on the basis of the quality and quantity of the expressed symptoms.

When considering such individuals on the first of these bases the term *subacute group* will be used, and the separate terms *neurosis* and *pseudoneurotic schizophrenia* will be employed when analyzing our data on the second basis, treating each group separately.

Pseudoneurotic schizophrenes

Access to this group for experimental purposes is rather difficult, since patients with this disorder are not usually hospitalized or resident in mental institutions. These patients come to the attention of psychiatrists in the course of private practice in psychiatry and sometimes through general medicine, but the most reliable and available source for study is found in the outpatient departments of psychiatric clinics. Even when pseudoneurotic schizophrenic patients are found in such clinics, it is difficult to study any large number of cases. The patients do not reside in one place so that a group may be identified and examined; the investigator must collect his data from patients accepted for treatment in the clinic as they are admitted. This is often a slow process, since psychotherapeutic treatment is time-consuming, and the number of new cases accepted for treatment is characteristically low at any given moment. The further restriction of selecting only cases about whom sufficient information

---

'borderline' cases are described and their symptomatology analyzed. It is suggested that these patients be classified 'pseudoneurotic form of schizophrenia.' "

This reaction appears similar to that described by the term, *schizophrenic reaction, chronic undifferentiated type,* as delimited by the Committee on Nomenclature and Statistics of the American Psychiatric Association (29). The brief description given by the committee permits some interpretation but is directed principally at delimiting the group described in greater detail by Hoch and Polatin.

is known to make firm diagnoses reduces the available cases even further.

The subgroup of pseudoneurotic schizophrenic patients studied in this investigation is composed of 27 patients, 6 males and 21 females, judged by the clinic staff to be so diagnosed upon acceptance. It would be helpful to be able to distinguish degrees of severity of behavior disturbance in this subgroup and to relate them to psychomotor test information, but this would be a much more difficult task than it is among chronic patients, whose symptoms are more easily observed and interpreted. The near-normality of this patient group reduces the range of symptom expression and would make the separation into grades of disease severity a difficult and uncertain procedure.

Neurotics

This group of patients, like the last, is small, and for exactly the same reasons. Patients accepted for treatment in an outpatient psychiatric clinic bearing a diagnosis of neurosis were examined as they became available. The subgroup is composed of 23 cases, 9 males and 14 females, judged to be neurotic by the clinic staff. Here again the difficulty of distinguishing grades of severity of disturbance in any clear fashion works against such stratification.

The two subgroups considered together comprise 50 patients, 15 males and 35 females, with an average age of 30.3 years and a range of 14.8 to 49.0 years. Although our current knowledge of pseudoneurotic schizophrenia is only at its beginning, there is general agreement that it represents a more morbid condition than neurosis, because of its essential linkage to schizophrenia. Considering the subacute group as a whole, then, it represents a degree of behavior disturbance somewhere between that of chronic schizophrenia and normality. When broken into subgroups, the two lie between these two points, with the probability of the neurotic being nearer to the normal and the pseudoneurotic schizophrene more in the direction of the chronic schizophrene. The various experimental subgroups, then, form a rough continuum ranging from the most severely disturbed behavior through moderate disorder to normal:

(Chronic)			(Subacute)		(Normal)
I	II	III	PNS	N	Norm

Grades I, II, and III of the chronic group refer to the severity rating as established by any or all of the three methods described, and pseudoneurotic schizophrenia is placed below neurosis by reason of its greater morbidity. It is probable that these steps are most unequal, for different methods of evaluation apply at each point.

PROCEDURES FOR THE PRESENTATION OF DATA

In presenting the observations recorded in this experiment the emphasis will be placed on graphic and tabular material rather than on a statistical treatment of group differences. There are several reasons for this. It is axiomatic in studies of mental disease that differences found between groups of patients or in a given patient from one time to another must be of some magnitude if they are to furnish an adequate index of prediction or status. This is a consequence of the fact that variation is the rule in mental illness, and for trends to be of more than temporary value they must be clear and strong. When they are found to be so they may be most simply presented by graphic methods. It is also known that the difficulty of access and the human and abnormal factors in the subject material itself are often such that a flat assumption of random selection of the sample from a total population of patients similarly afflicted cannot be made. For these reasons it has been thought best to pursue a policy of parsimony, making the fewest number of statistical assumptions necessary, and to represent the data in direct form as much as possible. Correlations are employed, and Fisher's "*t*" test of significance is used where groups are sufficiently large and homogeneous to justify this form of intergroup comparison. For the most part, however, learning curves, age curves, frequency distributions, graphic presentation of group means, and patterns of consistency appear to be the most adequate means of presentation.

PART II

Experimental Findings

CHAPTER 4

STUDIES WITH THE NORMAL

PRACTICE

THE procedures chosen for use with the experimental battery were designed to permit an inspection of the learning curve of performance for each of the fine psychomotor tasks. More than one purpose is served by concentration on the practice trials, but the primary reason for emphasis upon practice was for its effect upon the stability of the response.

Reaction time (lift)

Each subject performed 40 trials at this task, 20 serving as practice trials and 20 as the basis for the indicator of his reaction time. The *RT* (*L*) learning curve for the normal group is shown in Figure 4. The successive means of each 5 trials have been plotted, and are indicated by the numerals along the abscissa.

The scores on this test are measures of elapsed time. An improvement of performance with practice is shown by a gradual decay curve. It is apparent that this function is not strongly influenced by practice, and that most of the reduction in time of response which accompanies practice takes place in the first 15 trials, with a continuing very slight reduction spread over the 40 trials measured.

Reaction time (jump)

The procedure followed for *RT* (*J*) is the same as that for *RT* (*L*). The learning curve obtained is given in Figure 4. The scores on this test are also measures of elapsed time, and some improvement with practice may be seen in the gradual decay curve.

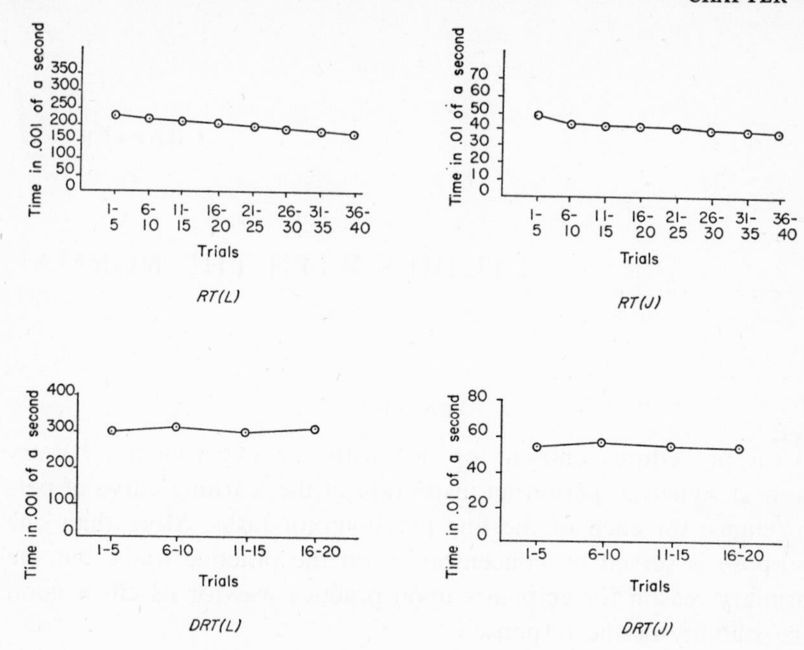

FIGURE 4. Learning curves on the tests of reaction time for the normal group (n = 194). Each point plotted represents the mean of 5 trials.

Most of the time reduction noted takes place during the first 15 trials, with a continuing very slight reduction over the 40 trials.

Tapping speed

Each subject performed 25 trials at this task, 15 serving as practice trials and 10 as the basis for the indicator of his speed of tapping. Figure 5 shows the learning curve of the normal group.

The scores for this test are measures of the number of individual taps made during a 5-second time interval, and improvement in performance is shown by a gradual growth function. Most of the increase in tapping rate which accompanies practice takes place during the first 10 trials, with a continuing slight gain throughout the 25 trials measured.

Dexterity

RIGHT HAND, LEFT HAND, AND BOTH HANDS. Each subject performed 3 trials at this task, 2 serving as practice trials and 1 as the indicator of dexterity with right and left and both hands. The

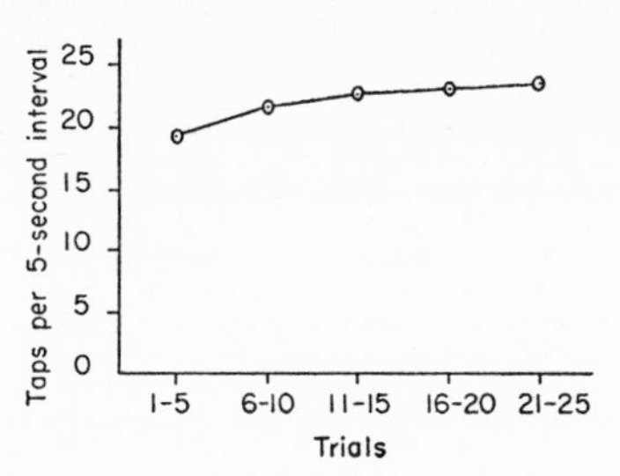

FIGURE 5. Learning curve on the tapping test for the normal group (n = 194). Each point plotted represents the mean of 5 trials.

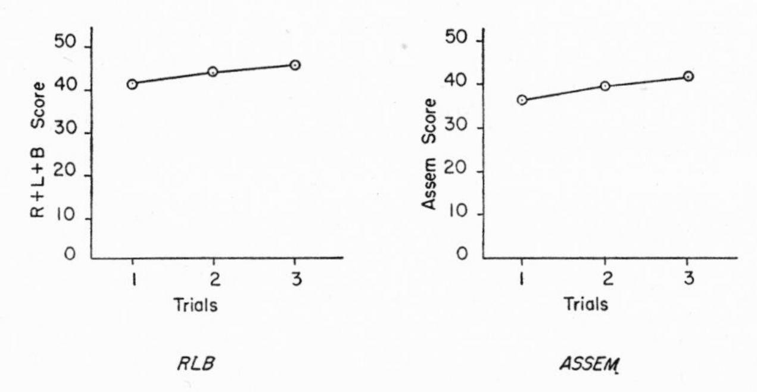

FIGURE 6. Learning curves on the dexterity tests for the normal group (n = 194). Each point plotted represents 1 trial.

learning curve of the normal group for *RLB* is shown in Figure 6.

The score for this test is the total number of pegs correctly inserted with right hand, left hand, and both hands, working in each manner for 30 seconds. An improvement in performance as a result of practice is seen on each trial, with most of the increase occurring on the second trial.

ASSEMBLY. On this task also, each subject performed 3 trials, 2 serving as practice and 1 as the indicator of dexterity in fine assembly. The learning curve of the normal group for *Assem* is shown in Figure 6. The score for this test is a count of the number of individual pieces assembled in 1 minute. An improvement in performance as a result of practice may be seen on each trial, with most of the increase occurring on the second trial.

Disjunctive reaction time (lift)

Each subject performed 20 trials at this task, 10 serving as practice and 10 as the basis for the indicator of discrimination reaction time. The *DRT (L)* learning curve is shown in Figure 4. The scores on this test are measures of elapsed time, and improvement in performance with practice would be shown by a gradual decay curve. It is apparent that practice has little effect upon this response, continued performance tending to lengthen very slightly, rather than shorten, the latency of response.

Disjunctive reaction time (jump)

The procedure followed is the same as that for *DRT (L)*. The learning curve is shown in Figure 4. The scores on this test are also measures of elapsed time, and an improvement with practice would be shown by a gradual decay curve. It is apparent that practice has little effect upon this response, since no major alterations occur upon extensive repetition.

An inspection of these learning curves makes it appear that practice exerts only a limited effect on these responses, and the gains with repetition are less than those characteristically seen where the entry of intelligence or work patterns into the response permits greater changes with increasing familiarity. Whether some gain in performance in the early stages of practice is visible or the curve remains essentially flat, it appears that a sufficiently stable plateau is reached for each task to permit a measurement of performance at a level approximating that which would be reached with greatly extended practice. A partial exception to this general statement must be taken for the finger-tip dexterity measures. The curves for *RLB* and *Assem* scores do not reach a plateau within the practice allowed, as was found to be the case in preliminary experimentation. The pilot work indicated that this response did level off at approximately the point reached on the third trial and on this basis the measure taken here is probably stable, but a more extensive practice series with this task would be desirable.

THE AGE FACTOR

The well-known influence of age upon fine psychomotor performance need not be extensively re-examined here, except to indicate the trend to slowed performance observed among the older subjects of this sample, to emphasize the need to consider the age factor in comparing performance by different experimental groups.

Figure 7 presents the age curves for each of the measures of

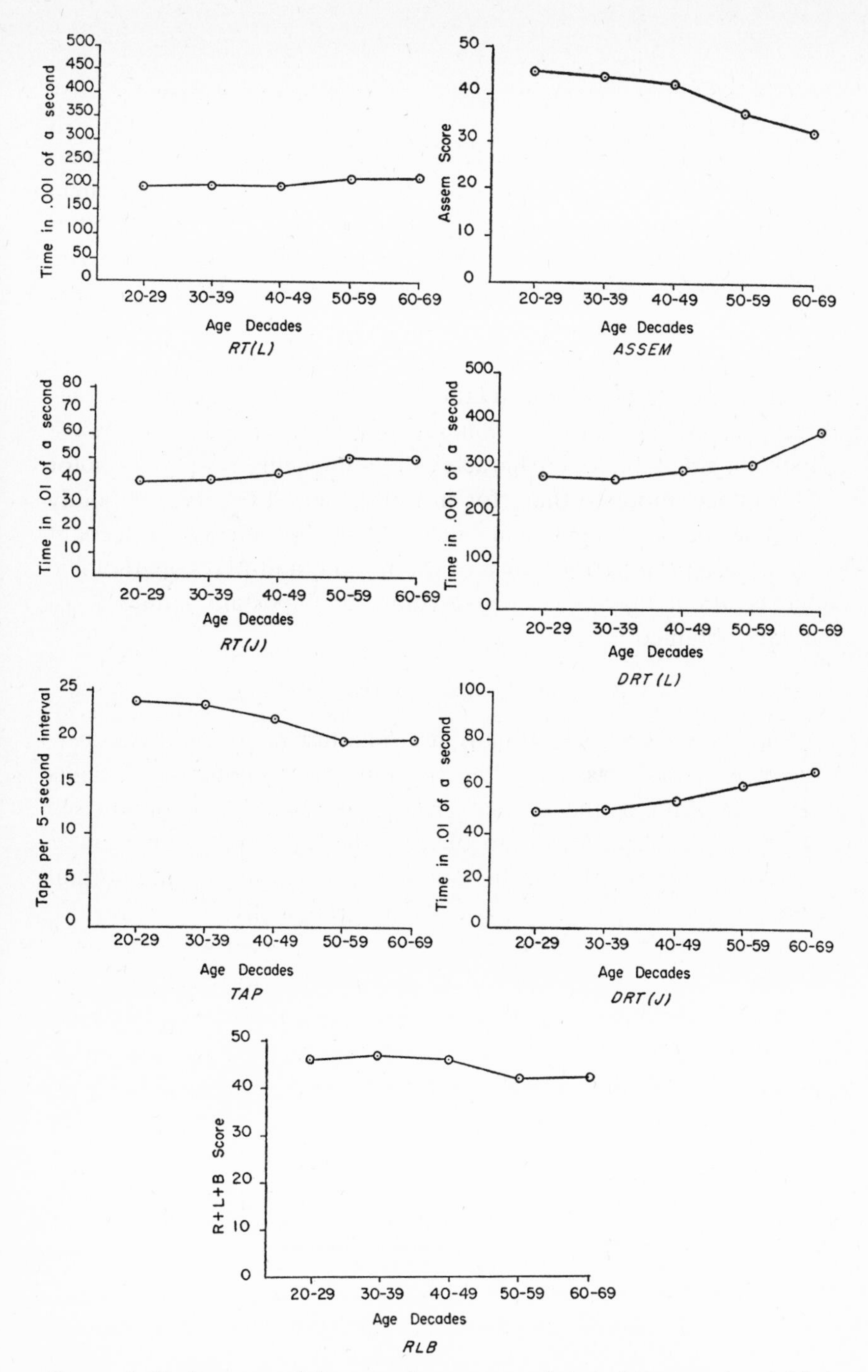

FIGURE 7. Performance of the normal group on each test of the experimental battery, by age decade (n total = 194).

the experimental battery, dividing the total normal group into five subgroups by age decade.

It is clear that a general tendency exists toward reduced performance as we go up the age scale, a finding which is in agreement with all other investigations of the relation of age to psychomotor performance (92). Some tasks show this tendency to a more marked degree than do others (i.e., *Tap, RLB, Assem, DRT* (*L*), and *DRT* (*J*) show proportionately greater losses with increased age than do *RT* (*L*) or *RT* (*J*)). These changes, added to what is known of the general interrelation of age and psychomotor performance, make it evident that the age of a subject is the most important single biologic characteristic influencing his psychomotor performance, more so than, for instance, race, I.Q., sex, or bodily size. The factor of age, then, must clearly be taken into account in comparing the performance of the normal and psychopathologic subjects, for it may be seen to exhibit an important influence on the data obtained.

THE SEX FACTOR

Some sex differences usually are manifest in psychomotor performance of all sorts, including the fine psychomotor movements (93). The data of the normal group have been divided into sex groups at each age decade to observe the influence of this factor on the data obtained throughout the age range of the normal sample. Figure 8 presents these results graphically.

In general, the performance curves of the two sex subgroups are very similar throughout the age range of the normal group, and no sharp differentiation appears among the several tests with regard to the general tendency toward the progressive slowing of responses with aging. The over-all results, given in Table 4 A, dividing the total group on the basis of sex alone, show only minor sex differences in the responses obtained. Males are slightly faster in performance on *RT* (*L*), *RT* (*J*), *Tap, DRT* (*L*), and *DRT* (*J*), and females are slightly faster in performance on the dexterity measures, *RLB* and *Assem*. Only the differences for *RT* (*J*) and *RLB* are statistically significant. A comparison by sex of the different age decade groups shows no major differences between the performance of the two sexes at the various age levels, with the notable exception of the *DRT* (*L*) and *DRT* (*J*) performance in

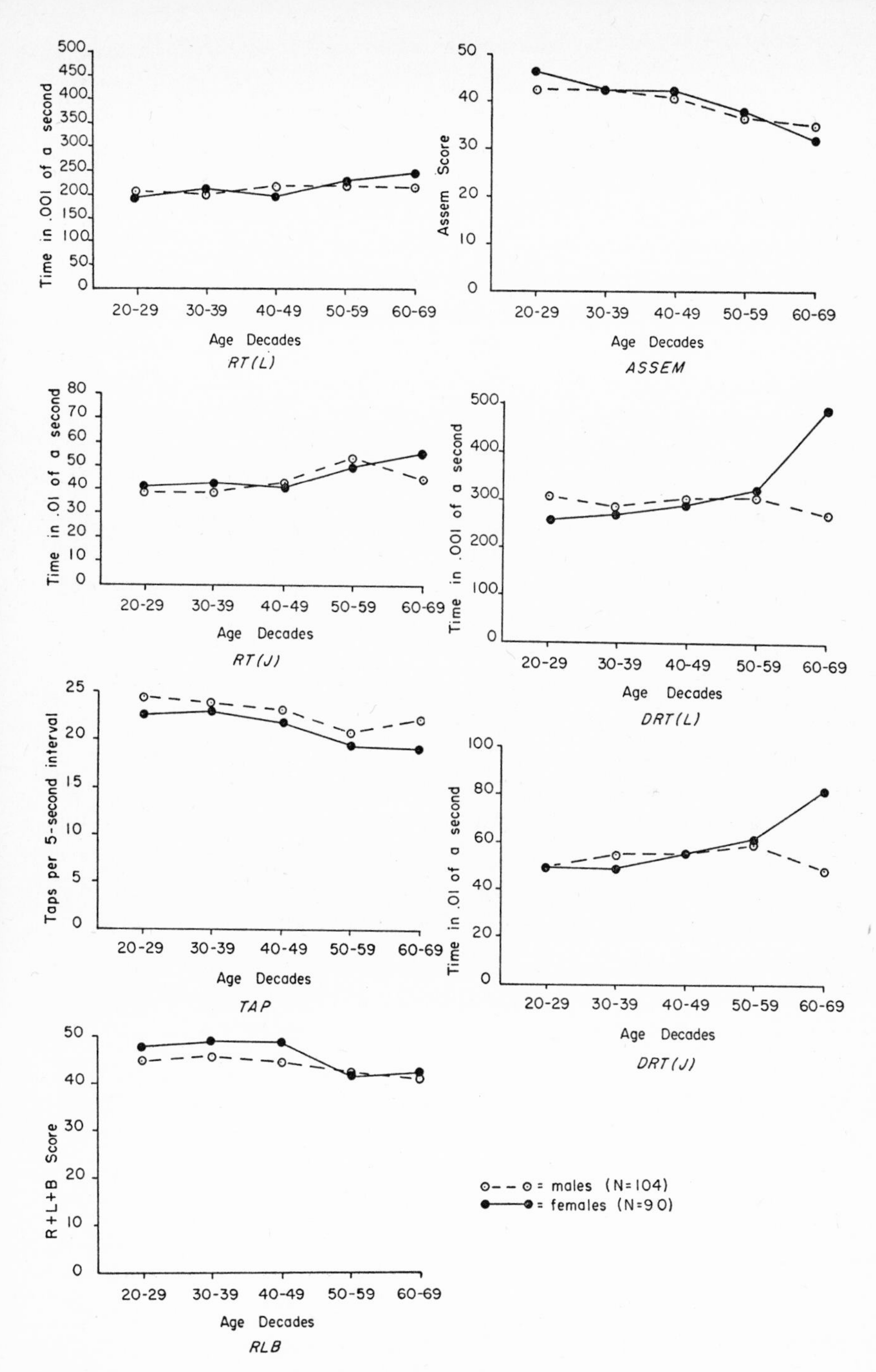

FIGURE 8. Performance of the normal group on each test of the experimental battery, by age decade and by sex (n total = 194).

TABLE 4. Means and standard deviations for the normal group on the tests of fine psychomotor movement

A. Males, females, and total group					B. Total group by age decades				
Test		*Males*	*Females*	*Total*	*20–29*	*30–39*	*40–49*	*50–59*	*60–69*
	n	104	90	194	44	55	44	26	25
RT (L)	M	209	209	209	200	202	203	226	233
	σ	33.0	37.0	34.7	30.6	23.8	32.4	47.9	31.5
RT (J)	M	42.3	45.7	44.0	40.3	41.1	42.9	51.0	50.6
	σ	7.6	7.0	7.5	4.9	4.7	5.1	9.6	8.1
Tap	M	23.3	21.8	22.6	23.9	23.6	22.5	20.2	20.9
	σ	3.5	2.7	3.3	2.6	2.4	3.2	3.2	4.0
RLB	M	44.5	46.6	45.6	46.4	47.1	46.6	42.1	42.1
	σ	4.0	5.0	4.6	4.1	4.4	4.8	3.8	1.9
Assem	M	41.2	41.2	41.2	44.5	43.5	41.9	36.8	33.4
	σ	6.4	6.5	6.4	6.0	5.4	5.1	5.7	1.8
DRT (L)	M	292	314	303	287	276	294	315	386
	σ	58.0	110.0	86.6	60.5	41.5	54.5	76.7	165.4
DRT (J)	M	54.0	60.5	57.2	51.5	54.0	56.2	62.9	68.4
	σ	8.9	15.1	12.6	6.0	6.3	8.9	11.4	23.6

the oldest group, 60–69 years. For unaccountable reasons, the female series between 60–69 years did very poorly on the tasks involving disjunctive reaction time, clearly diverging from their age curve as well as from the male group of comparable age. The performance of this group was not particularly irregular for the other measures, but was generally slower than might be expected, and perhaps reflects a sampling error.

In general, then, the sex factor, though apparent in the data, is rather slight. In view of the minor differences observed it seems feasible to treat the group as a whole, especially when comparisons are to be made to a sample which is similarly mixed.

TEST SCORES AND THEIR DISTRIBUTION

The scores for each individual on each test of the experimental battery have been computed on the basis of post-practice performance, as explained in Chapter 3 and above. Table 4 A presents the means and standard deviations for the total group, and for each sex separately.

The distribution of scores about their mean for each of the tests is presented graphically in Figure 9.[1]

[1] These curves have been smoothed once for clarity by the method of running averages, after histograms had been prepared for all original distributions, to make

It is clear that all the distributions obtained are gaussian in form, but it is worth noting that they tend to be slightly skewed away from the "physiologic limit," or presumed maximum performance. Presumably the level of performance is limited in the speed it may attain by structural considerations in the organism; note that this flattening is on the minimal end where elapsed time constitutes the measure (*RT* (*L*), *RT* (*J*), *DRT* (*L*), *DRT* (*J*)) and on the maximum end where performance in a given unit of time is the measure (*Tap*). This tendency does not seem to affect the dexterity scores, *RLB* and *Assem.*

Table 4 B presents the means and standard deviations for the normal group subdivided into five categories by age decade. The tendency toward greater reductions in performance with increased age is clearly visible in these data. An analysis of the standard deviations for performance at each age decade also shows a tendency toward an increase in group variability with increasing age, but this is not fully consistent.

Our pilot study indicated that responses made to the buzzer and to the bell were of a similar order, and a comparison of these responses in the total normal group has borne out this finding. Actually, a very small σ_D is obtained, owing chiefly to the high correlation of responses to the buzzer and bell (r_{zl} for *RT* (*L*) = + .91; r_{zl} for *RT* (*J*) = + .94), and it would require only a very small difference in response to the two stimuli to reach the point of statistical significance.

THE DISCRIMINATION FACTOR

The inclusion of disjunctive reaction time in the experimental battery was intended to get at the factor of "decision" or discrimination in getting the sample motions into action. This type of reaction is known to require longer than simple reaction time, the amount of the increase in latency being dependent upon the particular situation (140). Table 5 (page 58) gives the means for both simple and disjunctive reaction time for the total normal group, for each sex separately, and for the total group by age decades.

---

certain that the smoothing process produced no distortion and overlooked no possible implications in the raw data. The number of step intervals is somewhat different for different tests, depending upon the nature of the scores themselves. The intention was to divide each into approximately 12 step intervals.

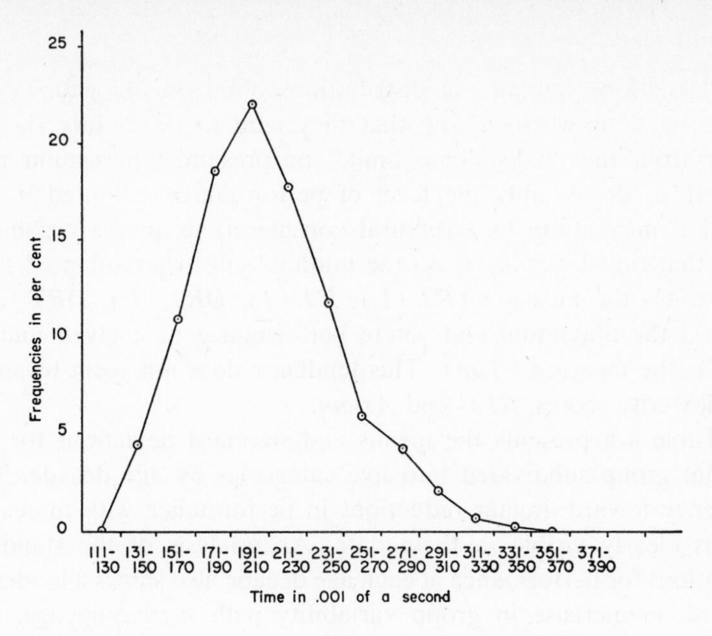

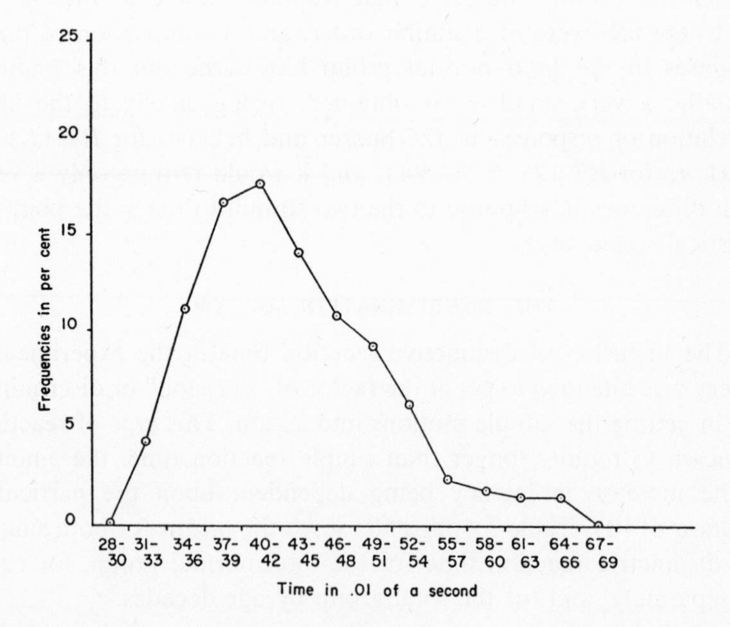

FIGURE 9. Distribution of scores on each test of the experimental battery for the normal group (n = 194).

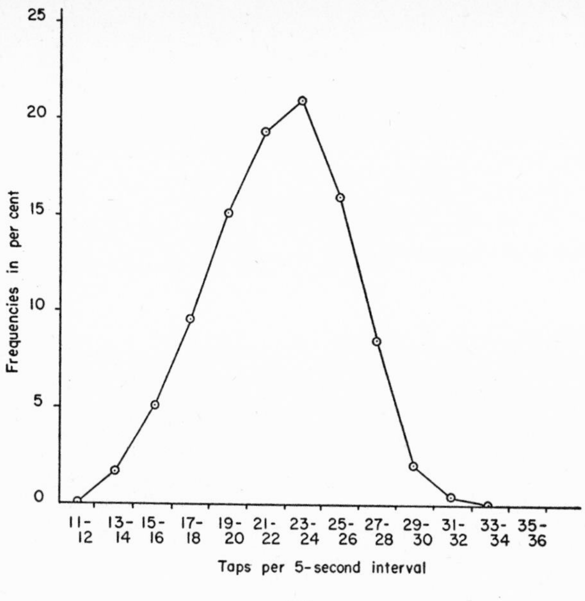

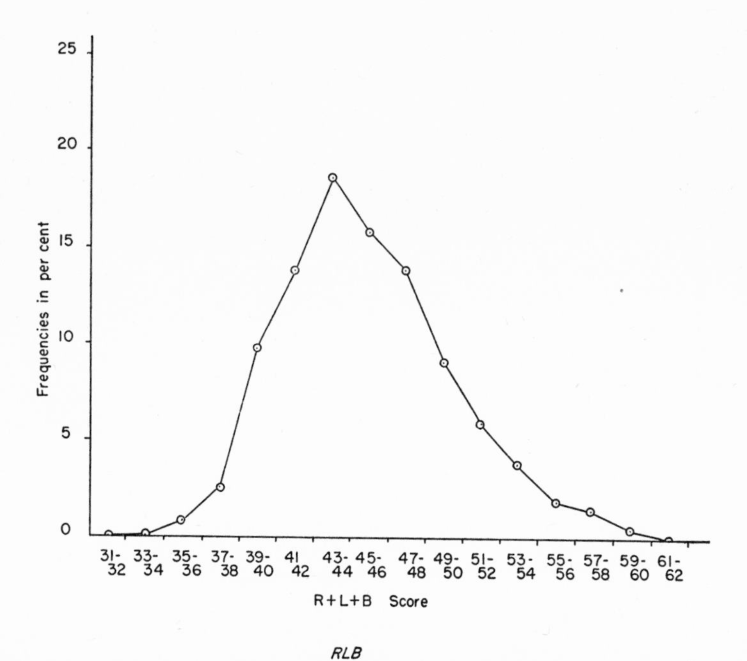

FIGURE 9 (*continued*). Distribution of scores on each test of the experimental battery for the normal group (n = 194).

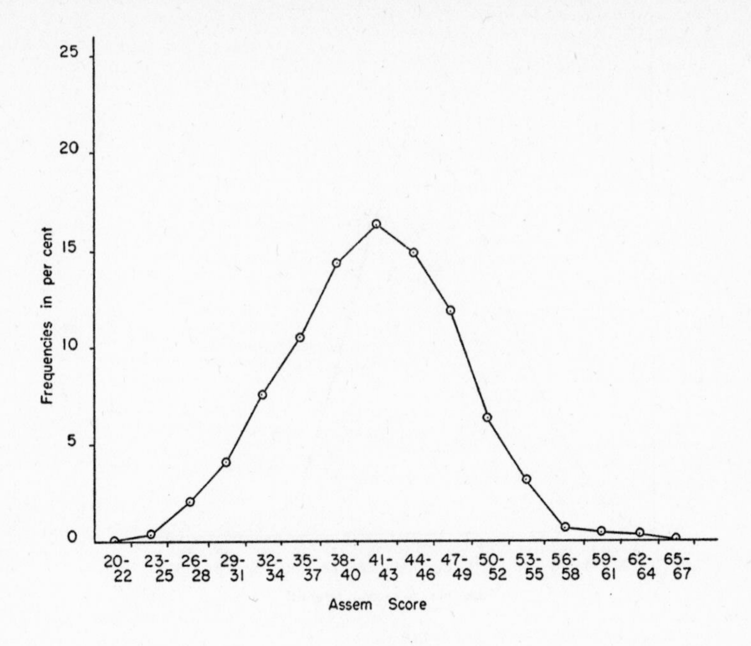

ASSEM

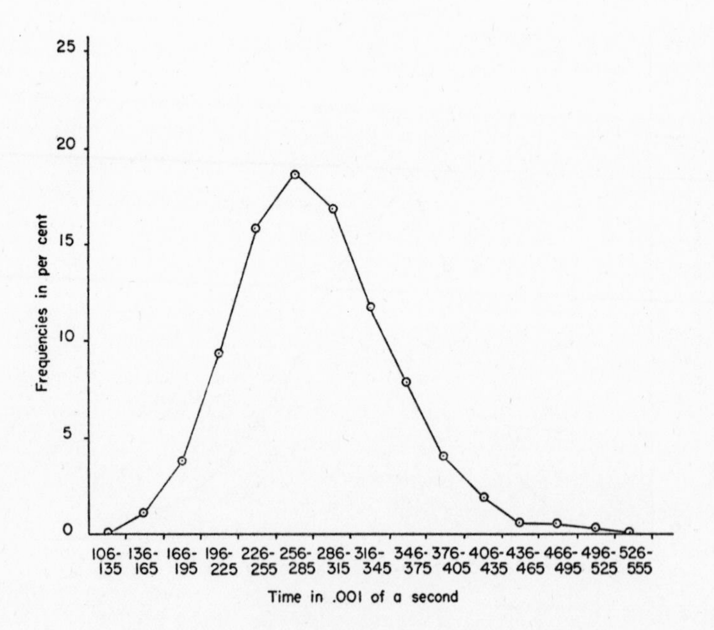

DRT (L)

FIGURE 9 (*continued*). Distribution of scores on each test of the experimental battery for the normal group (n = 194).

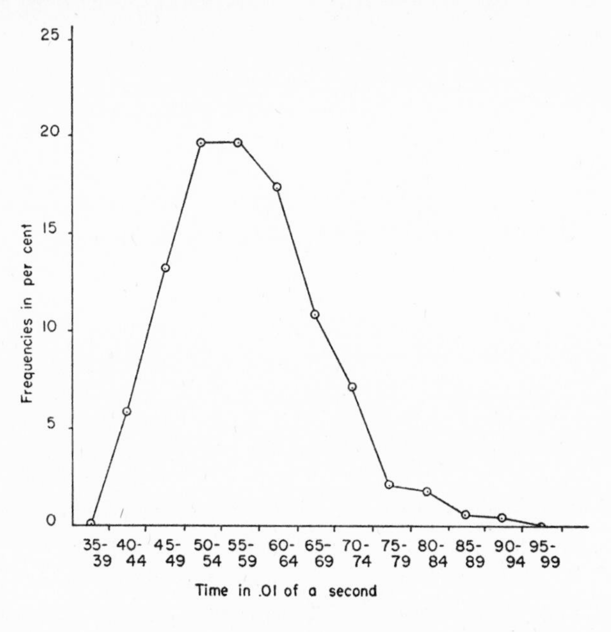

FIGURE 9 (*continued*). Distribution of scores on each test of the experimental battery for the normal group (n = 194).

To inspect the difference between the two types of reaction—simple and disjunctive reaction time—we may calculate a difference score in which the time required for the simple response is subtracted from that required for the discrimination response. Difference scores are shown in Table 5 for both lift and jump reaction times. It is clear that the disjunctive reaction takes longer, about 95 ms. longer for *DRT* (*L*) and 13 hundredths of a second longer for *DRT* (*J*). A fairly wide departure from this value occurs for the oldest age group examined. Because the basic score, the simple reaction, may be increased by age or other factors, the relation of simple to disjunctive reaction time may best be represented by a ratio, rather than by a difference score, to take into account those variables in the more complex disjunctive reaction in a way proportional to their influence on simple reaction time. These ratios are also given in Table 5. The ratio for the total group is .69 for *RT* (*L*)/*DRT* (*L*) and .77 for *RT* (*J*)/*DRT* (*J*), and subdivision by age and sex produces values not appreciably different.

TABLE 5. Simple and disjunctive reaction time means for the normal group

Group	*n*	*RT (L)*	*DRT (L)*	*diff*	*RT (L) / DRT (L)*	*RT (J)*	*DRT (J)*	*diff*	*RT (J) / DRT (J)*
Total	194	209	303	94	.69	44.0	57.2	13.2	.77
Males	104	209	292	83	.72	42.3	54.0	11.7	.78
Females	90	209	314	105	.66	45.7	60.5	14.8	.75
Age groups									
20–29	44	200	287	87	.70	40.3	51.5	11.2	.78
30–39	55	202	276	74	.73	41.1	54.0	12.9	.76
40–49	44	203	294	91	.69	42.9	56.2	13.3	.76
50–59	26	226	315	89	.71	51.0	62.9	11.9	.81
60–69	25	233	386	153	.60	50.6	68.4	17.8	.74

INTERRELATION OF THE TESTS

It is important to know the extent to which the different tests of fine psychomotor movement included in the experimental battery relate to one another, so that some idea may be formed about their similarities and differences in performance, and to observe to what extent the different tasks are related in the normal group as a base for further comparisons with the data of psychopathologic subjects. Table 6 A shows the degree of intercorrelation present when the performance of all subjects in the normal group is analyzed.

This matrix, which is a way of listing the extent to which performance on any given test of the experimental battery relates to performance on all other tests, shows that all of the test intercorrelations obtained are positive.[1] Most individual tests show only a low or moderate degree of interrelation, but a few rather high correlation coefficients are included. These high coefficients represent the interrelation of those tasks which were thought to be related to the same factor (see page 14); i.e., all of the tasks relating to Factor I, the speed of initiating single reactions (*RT* (*L*), *RT* (*J*), *DRT* (*L*) and *DRT* (*J*)), are strongly interrelated; and the two tasks relating to Factor III, finger dexterity (*RLB* and *Assem*), are also clearly interrelated. The coefficients listed in Table 6 B are the intercorrelations of the "key" measures, or those single tests most nearly

[1] In constructing this table, those tests scored in terms of elapsed time have been reflected to express all performance in one direction, i.e., so that larger numerical scores indicate faster performance, to reduce the need for individual interpretation of the sign of each correlation coefficient.

TABLE 6. Performance of the normal group on the tests of fine psychomotor movement (n = 194)

A. Correlation matrix

Tests	*RT (L)*	*RT (J)*	*Tap*	*RLB*	*Assem*	*DRT (L)*	*DRT (J)*
RT (L)	—	.78	.44	.39	.37	.64	.55
RT (J)		—	.52	.25	.35	.54	.70
Tap			—	.21	.28	.29	.39
RLB				—	.61	.35	.23
Assem					—	.35	.30
DRT (L)						—	.70
DRT (J)							—

B. Intercorrelations of key tests

	Tap	*Assem*
RT (L)	.44	.37
Tap		.28

describing the three basic factors under study. These have been taken from Table 6 A to emphasize the finding that the different factors do indeed appear to be somewhat independent and that the results of this sample appear to bear out the preliminary factor analyses of many different tests of fine psychomotor abilities in that only low or moderate relationships obtain between the three essential emergent factors.

COMPARISON OF THE NORMAL GROUP DATA WITH OTHER STUDIES

A brief statement on the comparison of data obtained on the normal sample by the specific techniques of this experiment with the reports of other workers may help to relate these results more closely to the large body of fine psychomotor data existing in the psychologic literature. The principal need for translation centers about the measures of the speed of initiating a single response, which involves a somewhat different procedure than is usual. In "classical" reaction time experiments the task of the subject is usually to lift his finger upon first becoming aware of a stimulus signal. In this experiment this has been modified to require the subject to initiate a thrust movement upon hearing a signal, that is, to lift his finger from a resting point, traverse a short distance, and press down a key. Reaction time is measured as the period of time which elapses between the start of the auditory signal and lift of the finger from the rest point to begin the movement instructed. It appears, then, that both the type of response required and the mental set are different, and that these factors may exert an influence on the data recorded. As the general aim of this series of experiments is to compare performance by different experimental groups, such a constant factor would in no way invalidate comparative studies, but in the interest of relating the data to the more usual procedure in reaction time studies the following experiment was performed. A small series of 12 normal subjects performed a series of trials first by the method of this experiment and then by the "classical" method (simple lift in response to the stimulus). Averaged results were as follows:

"Classical" method	147 ms.
This method	201 ms.

These results indicate that the "classical" method leads to a more rapid response, on the average 54 ms. faster. If we take the fraction obtained here, for purposes of approximation only, and apply it as a correction factor to the value obtained for the *RT* (*L*) of the total normal group:

Normal group average *RT* (*L*)	209 ms.
Difference factor (from above)	— 54 ms.
	155 ms.

the resulting estimate of 155 ms. is comparable to values usually reported for simple auditory reaction time of approximately 150 ms. (65).

There is greater uncertainty about the tapping rates usually reported, as a result of the use of different apparatus and procedure by different investigators. The values obtained with the procedure of this investigation fall below the figure of 33 taps per 5-second interval given by King and Clausen (66) as a rough average of the reports of many investigators, but are similar to the values given by some workers employing a similar type of apparatus. For example, Shakow and Huston (123) report 28.9 taps per 5-second interval, and the mean for this method is 22.6 taps per 5-second interval.

The dexterity measures of *RLB* and *Assem* obtained on the normal group are in close approximation to the values reported with this technique by its authors, Tiffin and Asher (133):

	RLB	*Assem*
Tiffin and Asher	50.7	44.7
This study	45.6	41.2

The group reported by Tiffin and Asher (n = 434) were of college age, and their performance would be expected to be somewhat higher than the normal group of this study, with an average age of 42.2 years. Very similar scores were achieved by the youngest normal group of this study (age decade 20–29 years) and the college age normals reported by Tiffin and Asher.

SAMPLE NORMAL PERFORMANCE

The detailed record of a specific individual from the normal group may help to form an idea of what characteristic post-practice performance on the test battery by a normal individual looks like:

Subject No. 338 is a female, thirty years of age, a housewife and part-time elementary school teacher. She is a college graduate, married, has three children.

TESTS

Trials	*RT (L)*	*RT (J)*	*Tap*	*RLB*	*Assem*	*DRT (L)*	*DRT (J)*
1	164	36	22	46	41	318	63
2	216	54	23			251	53
3	208	41	23			239	61
4	223	44	24			298	69
5	231	42	23			296	57
6	172	33	24			358	65
7	183	39	24			313	53
8	190	37	24			248	51
9	168	31	25			260	49
10	181	34	24			252	53
11	177	39					
12	174	38					
13	171	34					
14	169	37					
15	172	37					
16	166	33					
17	199	40					
18	204	41					
19	172	34					
20	207	37					
Mean	187.3	38.5	23.6	46	41	283.3	57.4
σ	20.3	4.9	0.8			37.2	6.4

Some scatter in performance is, of course, observable within tests with multiple trials; the standard deviation computed for the individual's performance gives some idea of this spread.

SUMMARY OF FINDINGS ON THE NORMAL GROUP

The pattern of performance given by the normal group on tests of the experimental battery described in the foregoing sections provides the necessary base-line information against which to compare the performance of psychopathologic groups. It is important that a clear notion is formed of what may be expected in the way of normal performance so that deviations from the norm may be readily identified. To begin with, the form and rate of improved performance consequent upon practice at the tasks has been shown to be a demonstrable and regular effect. The improvement is chiefly apparent early in the practice series, and all responses are found to reach a relatively stable level within the period of observation. Both familiarity with the tasks and learning factors thus do have an effect upon the data obtained, but by careful observation of this process at work we may see that such effects are rendered minimal by the time of recording each sample measure.

The age of the subject may clearly be seen to be reflected in performance on these tasks of fine psychomotor movement. A gradual, regular loss of function with increasing age is a well-known characteristic of psychomotor performance for subjects in the age range tested here, and performance by the normal group of this study demonstrates this effect at work. It is obvious from these data that age exerts a significant influence upon the performance on the test battery and is a primary factor to be taken into account when contrasting the performance of experimental groups. The sex of the subject may also be seen to influence performance on tests of the battery to some extent, males being somewhat faster on reaction time and tapping tasks and females somewhat faster on dexterity tests. These differences have been found to be relatively slight, however, and if the sex ratios within experimental groups are similar to that of the normal group, the effect of this factor may be simply neutralized.

The scores obtained by the normal group on the post-practice measures on each test of the battery have been collected and presented in both tabular and graphic form (Tables 4–6; Figures 4–9) to serve as a basis for comparison with the other experimental groups. Average scores and the distribution of scores about mean performance for the total group, for each sex separately and for the total group divided into age decades, provide a measuring stick against which to compare the data of other experimental groups. When we examine these scores to observe the characteristic interrelation of tests within the experimental battery it is clear that although a positive relationship does exist between tests of the different basic factors, it is either low or moderate, indicating that these are sampling rather independent properties of fine psychomotor ability. The higher correlations among different tests of the same factor, of course, indicate their essential linkage in terms of performance by the normal group as well as through the logical basis upon which they were selected.

A comparison of simple and disjunctive reaction time performance has been introduced into the test battery because our previous knowledge of such performance indicated that more time is required to perform such a simple discrimination response. The performance of the normal group bears out this assumption and furnishes an index of the proportional increase in time over that for simple response which will serve as the base for a similar comparison of the data from other experimental groups. This will permit an answer to the question of the effect of introducing an elementary difficulty into simple fine psychomotor response.

The comparison of the data of the normal group with those of studies by other investigators indicates that very similar values are obtained in our normal group, and should serve as an assurance that the measures of this experimental battery are testing the same fundamental human processes which have been the subject of psychologic investigation in other contexts.

In brief, the characteristic pattern of normal performance on tests of the experimental battery described in this chapter should serve as an adequate base line for the comparison of performance by psychopathologic groups, and the grasp of what constitutes normal performance should enable us to observe in considerable detail whether or not the performance of psychopathologic patients deviates from these levels of average performance, characteristic variability, and patterns of interrelation among the separate tests.

CHAPTER 5

STUDIES WITH CHRONIC SCHIZOPHRENES

THE test procedures employed with this group are identical with those described for the normal group.

PRACTICE

An inspection of the learning curves of performance by the chronic group on the several tasks of the experimental battery shows the learning process to be an orderly one, much like that observed in the normal group. Following very similar courses, both groups achieve relative stability of response after the same number of practice trials. The learning curves of the normal group have been repeated in the figures exemplifying learning by the chronic group to permit direct comparison of the two groups (Figures 10–12). The scores on which these plots are based have been corrected for apparatus error, but are uncorrected for age or sex, as the normal and chronic groups are of comparable average age and range and are composed of equal or approximately equal numbers of male and female subjects.

Reaction time (lift)

The practice curve of the chronic group for the *RT* (*L*) is given in Figure 10.

It is apparent that this function is not strongly influenced by practice in the chronic group and that no clear reduction in time of response accompanies practice to the extent given. The curve for performance by the chronic group is much more irregular than that obtained from normal subjects, particularly in the first trials at the second sitting (trials 21–25).

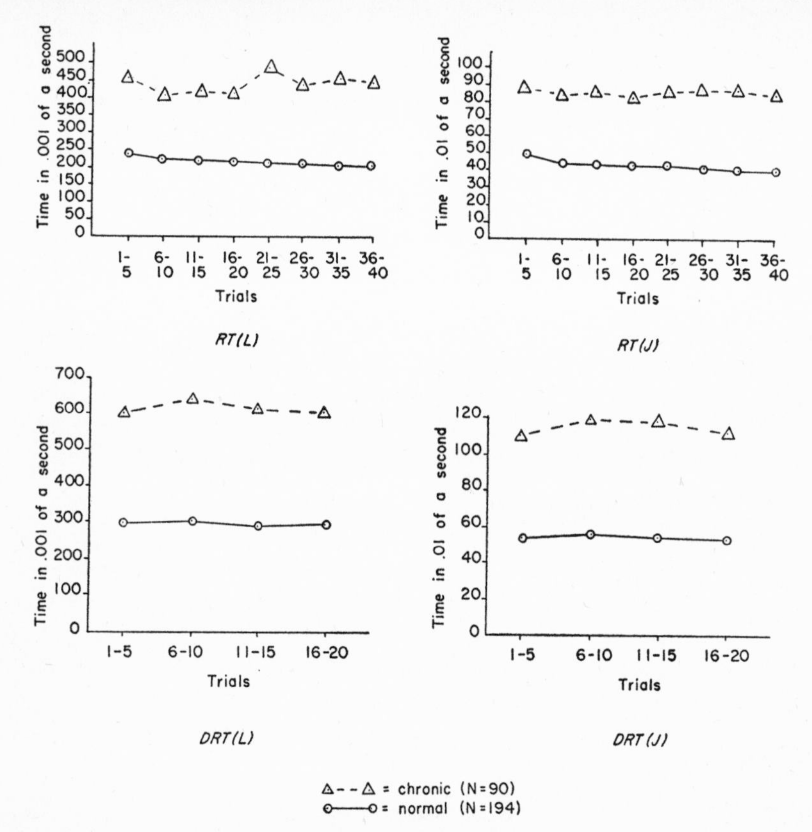

FIGURE 10. Learning curves on tests of reaction time for the chronic and normal groups. Each point plotted represents the mean of 5 trials.

Reaction time (jump)

The practice curve of the chronic group for the *RT (J)* task is given in Figure 10. A slight reduction in the time of response as a result of repeated performance may be noted, most of which takes place during the first 15 trials. Here, again, a somewhat greater irregularity in performance by the chronic group is apparent than was found with normal subjects.

Tapping speed

The practice curve of the chronic group for tapping speed is given in Figure 11.

A gradual growth function indicates improvement in perform-

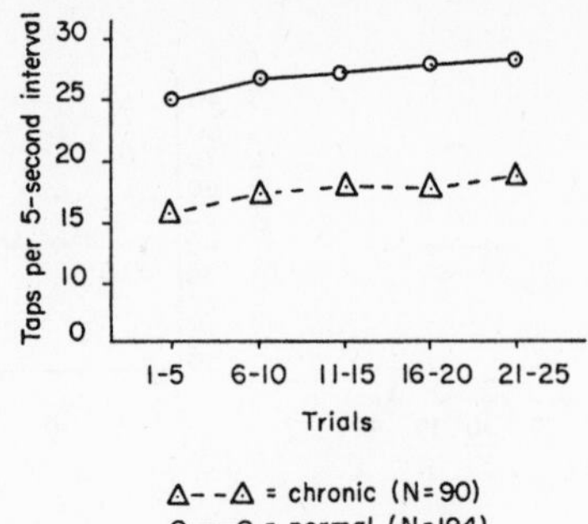

FIGURE 11. Learning curves on the tapping test for the chronic and normal groups. Each point plotted represents the mean of 5 trials.

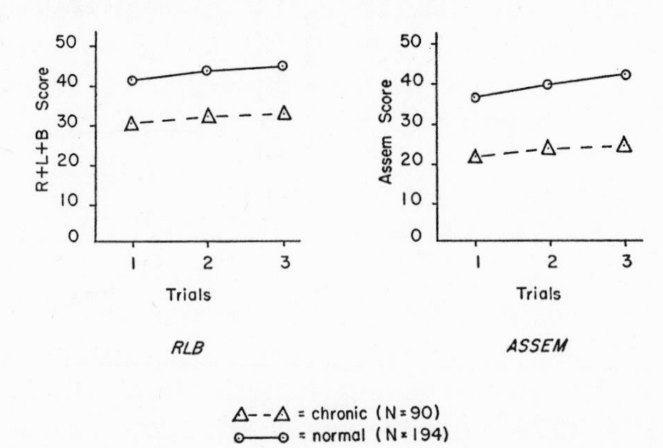

FIGURE 12. Learning curves on the dexterity tests for the chronic and normal groups. Each point plotted represents one trial.

ance, most of which takes place during the first 10 trials, with a continuing slight gain throughout the 25 trials measured.

Dexterity

RIGHT HAND, LEFT HAND, AND BOTH HANDS. The practice curve for performance on the *RLB* dexterity measure by the chronic group is shown in Figure 12. An improvement in performance may be seen with each trial. The restricted number of trials at this longer task does not permit as adequate a notation of the learning process as is possible with other measures; despite this limitation a gain in performance may be observed and a levelling off of response is begun within the few trials given.

ASSEMBLY. The practice curve for the chronic group on the assembly task is also shown in Figure 12.

A definite improvement in performance as a result of practice may be seen on each trial, with about equal gains occurring on the second and third trials. Here, again, the limited number of repetitions does not permit a complete view of the learning process or of the stabilization of response.

Disjunctive reaction time (*lift*)

The practice curve for the chronic group on the task of discrimination reaction time is shown in Figure 10. An initial slowing of performance on the first 10 trials is followed by a reduction from this increased time of response to a level approximating that shown in the first 5 responses. Practice does not appear to reduce the elapsed time of response within the period observed.

Disjunctive reaction time (*jump*)

The practice curve for the chronic group on the jump response in the discrimination situation is shown in Figure 10. A phenomenon similar to that noted for *DRT* (*L*) is observed: an initial slowing of response followed by improvement to the approximate level of the first 5 responses. Again, it appears that practice in the amounts given here does not serve to reduce the elapsed time of response.

The similarity of the learning curves for the normal and chronic groups is striking, both for performance on individual tasks and for the series as a whole. It would appear that despite a tendency to a greater irregularity of response on tests of reaction time, the essential picture is one of a series of responses acquired in a similar fashion by both the normal and psychopathologic group. The level of stability in response achieved and shown in these curves seems adequate to permit measurement at a level approximating that which would be reached with greatly extended practice. For the measures of finger-tip dexterity the same exception to this general statement must be taken as was made for the normal group, since the practice curves for the chronic group describe a similar course (see page 47).

TABLE 7. Means and standard deviations for the chronic and normal groups on the tests of fine psychomotor movement

Test		Chronic group ($n = 90$)	Normal group ($n = 194$)
RT (L)	M	449	209
	σ	263	34.7
RT (J)	M	88.9	44.0
	σ	39.0	7.5
Tap	M	13.5	22.6
	σ	6.1	3.3
RLB	M	33.5	45.6
	σ	6.4	4.6
Assem	M	24.6	41.2
	σ	8.7	6.4
DRT (L)	M	611	303
	σ	315	86.6
DRT (J)	M	116.5	57.2
	σ	62.0	12.6

TEST SCORES AND THEIR DISTRIBUTION

The psychomotor performance scores for the chronic group on each test of the experimental battery have been computed on the basis of post-practice performance, and Table 7 presents the means and standard deviations on all tests of the battery for the total chronic group. The scores of the normal group have also been repeated in this table to aid in the direct comparison with performance by the chronic group.

The differences between the mean values obtained for the chronic and normal groups are immediately apparent, with performance by the chronic group showing markedly slower response on all tests of the experimental battery. This comparison is dealt with at length in the section to follow. The inter-individual variability of the chronic group is larger for all tasks and is dramatically expanded for the several measures of reaction time. A better idea of the distribution of scores on each test may be had from the graphic plots shown in Figure 13, which also repeat the distribution curves of the normal group to facilitate direct comparison.

An extraordinary spread may be observed in the distribution of scores for all of the tasks relating to the initiating of a single response, *RT (L)*, *RT (J)*, *DRT (L)*, and *DRT (J)*. The curves are far too flat to be described by the usual terms, though all show some degree of central tendency with fewer cases at the extremes. The distributions of scores for all other tasks, *Tap, RLB,* and *Assem,* are found to be rather flat, but generally gaussian in form.

COMPARISON OF TEST SCORES WITH THOSE OF THE NORMAL GROUP

It is clear that major differences exist between the performance of the chronic group and that of normal subjects on all tests of the battery. These differences may be seen in the mean scores achieved by each of these groups (Table 7) and in the distribution plots illustrating the spread of scores in the two groups (Figure 13). Several aspects of this definite contrast in performance are worth noting. The most striking feature, and perhaps the most meaningful, is the fact that the groups differ in several ways: in average performance, in range of performance, and, to a certain extent, in variability of performance. Some overlap is present in the distribution of the groups on each test, of course, but the separation of means is clear and unmistakable. In each instance the difference indicates a retarded and more variable performance by members of the chronic group. The degree of retardation shows a certain constancy, despite the fact that the tests represent measures of different elements of psychomotor ability, in that performance scores by the chronic group are roughly one-half those established by a normal group of comparable age and sex. The expanded variability in the chronic group on tasks of initiating single reactions is no less striking for these tests than is the difference between their mean values, and these two ways of describing performance are probably related in this instance. The extreme spreading on the side of the distribution indicating slowed response directs attention to the fact that the nature of the increased spread for the total group actually lies in this direction and is caused by great increases in time of response which are not accompanied by corresponding decreases in time of response. The chronic group performance on tasks other than those of reaction time does not show a similar pattern of increase in inter-individual variability, and, although the standard deviations for the tapping and dexterity scores are larger than those noted for the normal group, they do not demonstrate the striking spread observed on tests of the reaction time factor. An analysis of the group was made by individual subjects to ascertain the extent

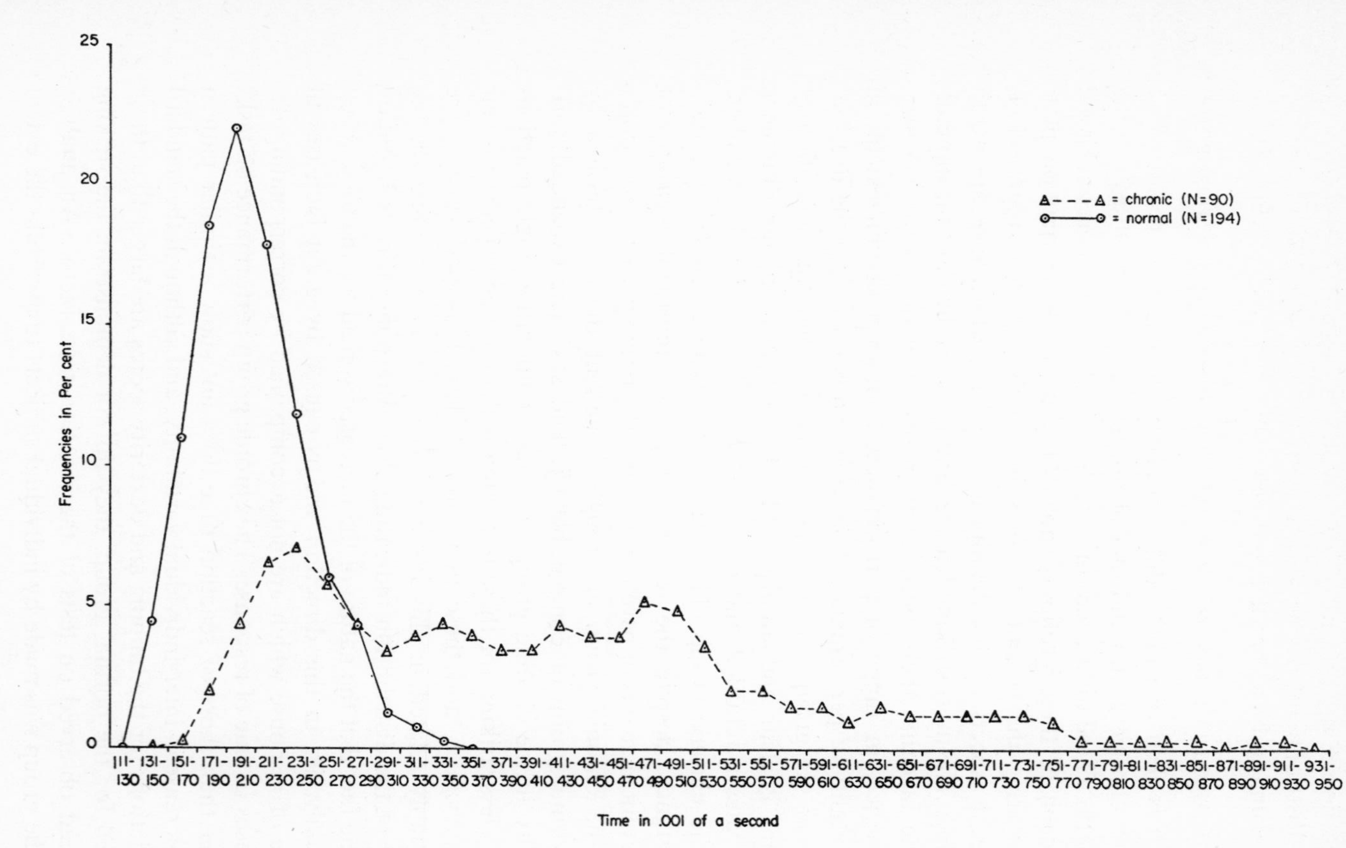

FIGURE 13. Distribution of scores on each test of the experimental battery for the chronic and normal groups.

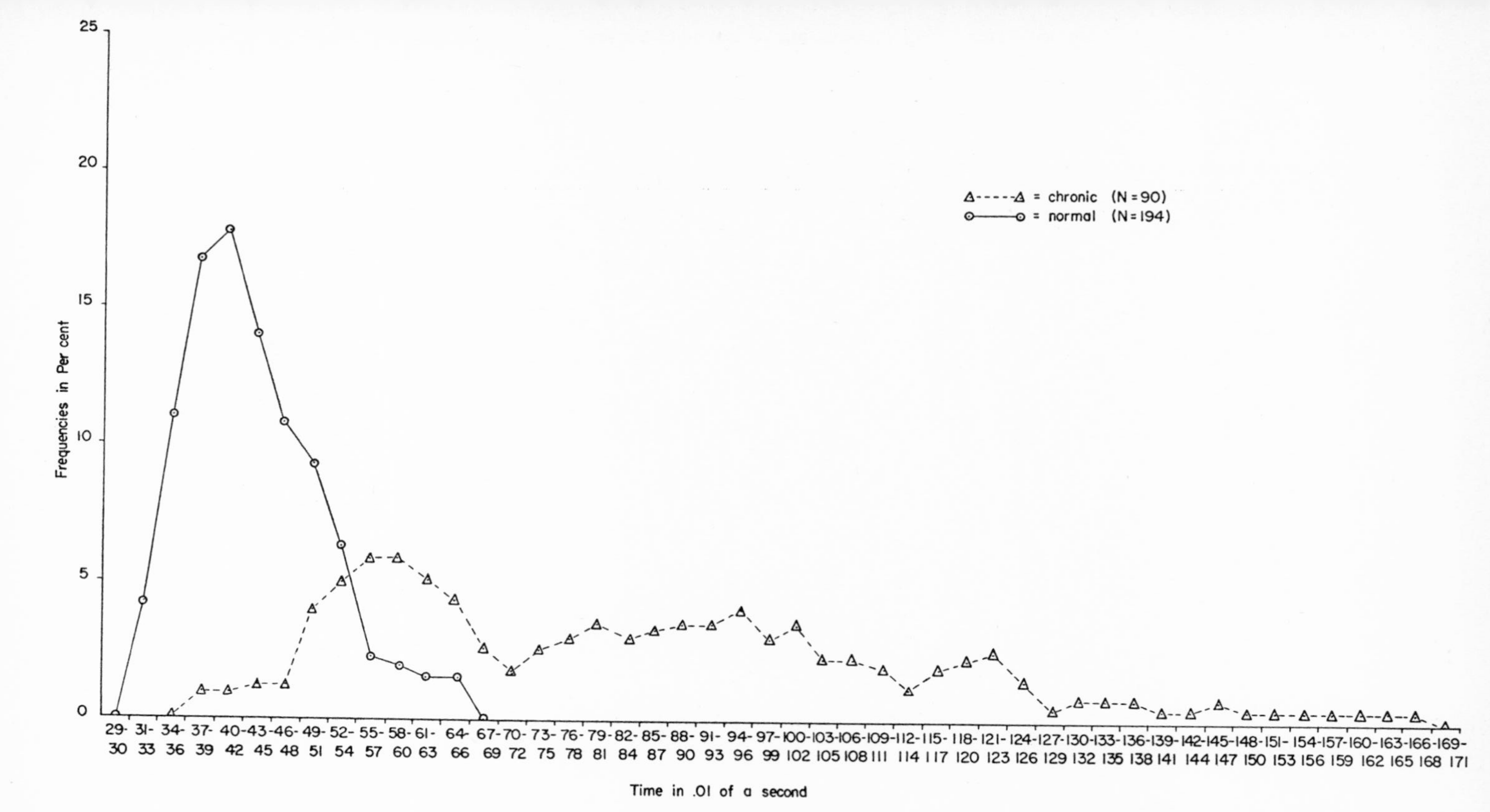

FIGURE 13 (*continued*). Distribution of scores on each test of the experimental battery for the chronic and normal groups.

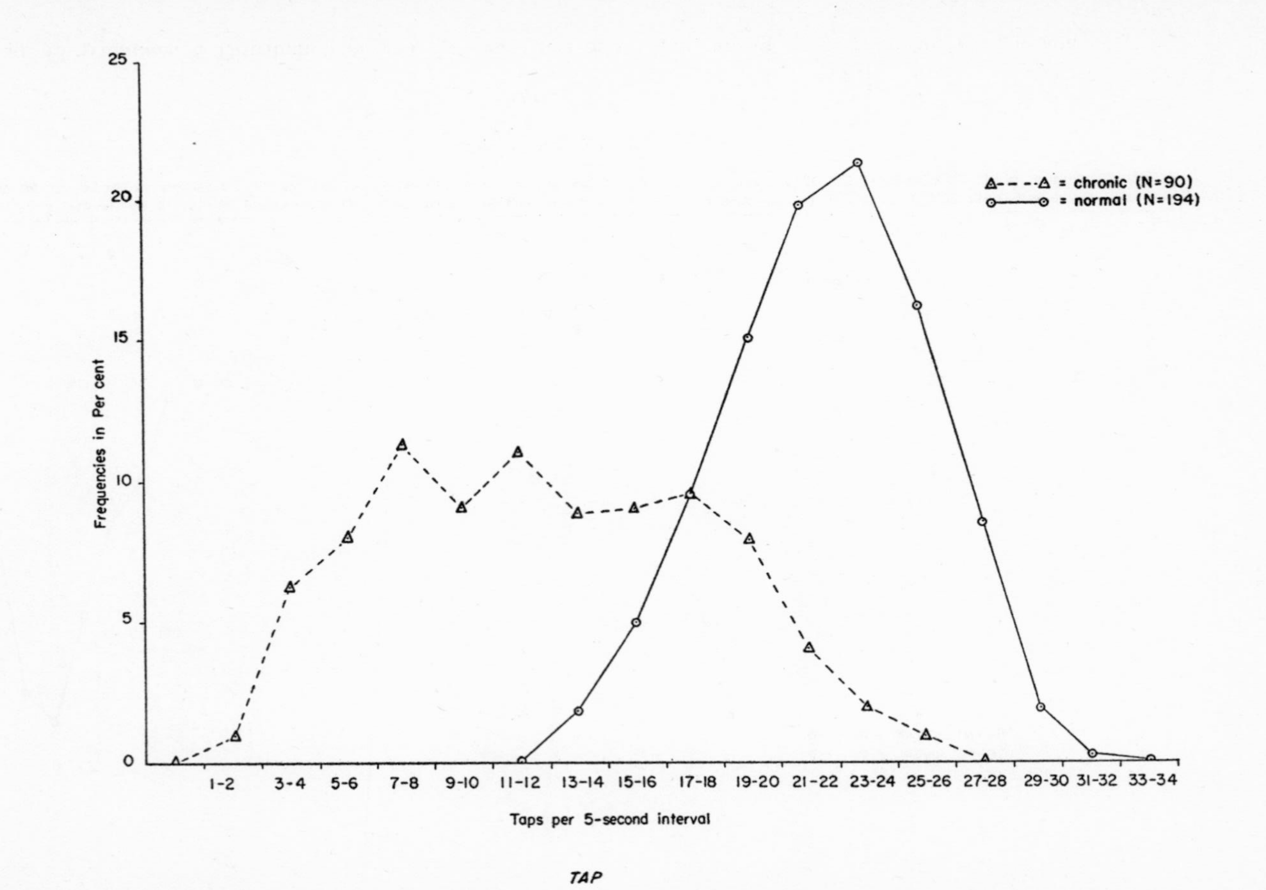

FIGURE 13 (*continued*). Distribution of scores on each test of the experimental battery for the chronic and normal groups.

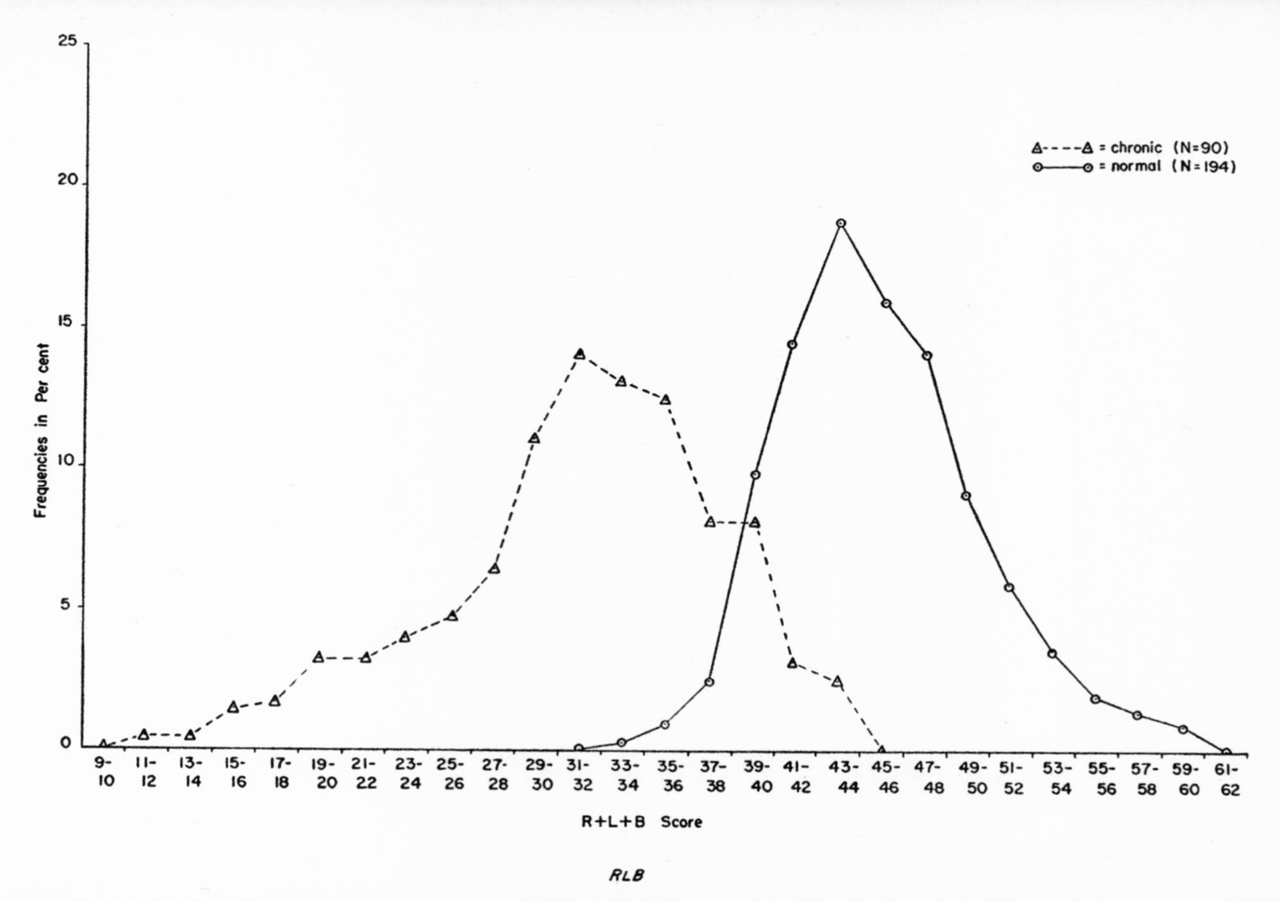

FIGURE 13 (*continued*). Distribution of scores on each test of the experimental battery for the chronic and normal groups.

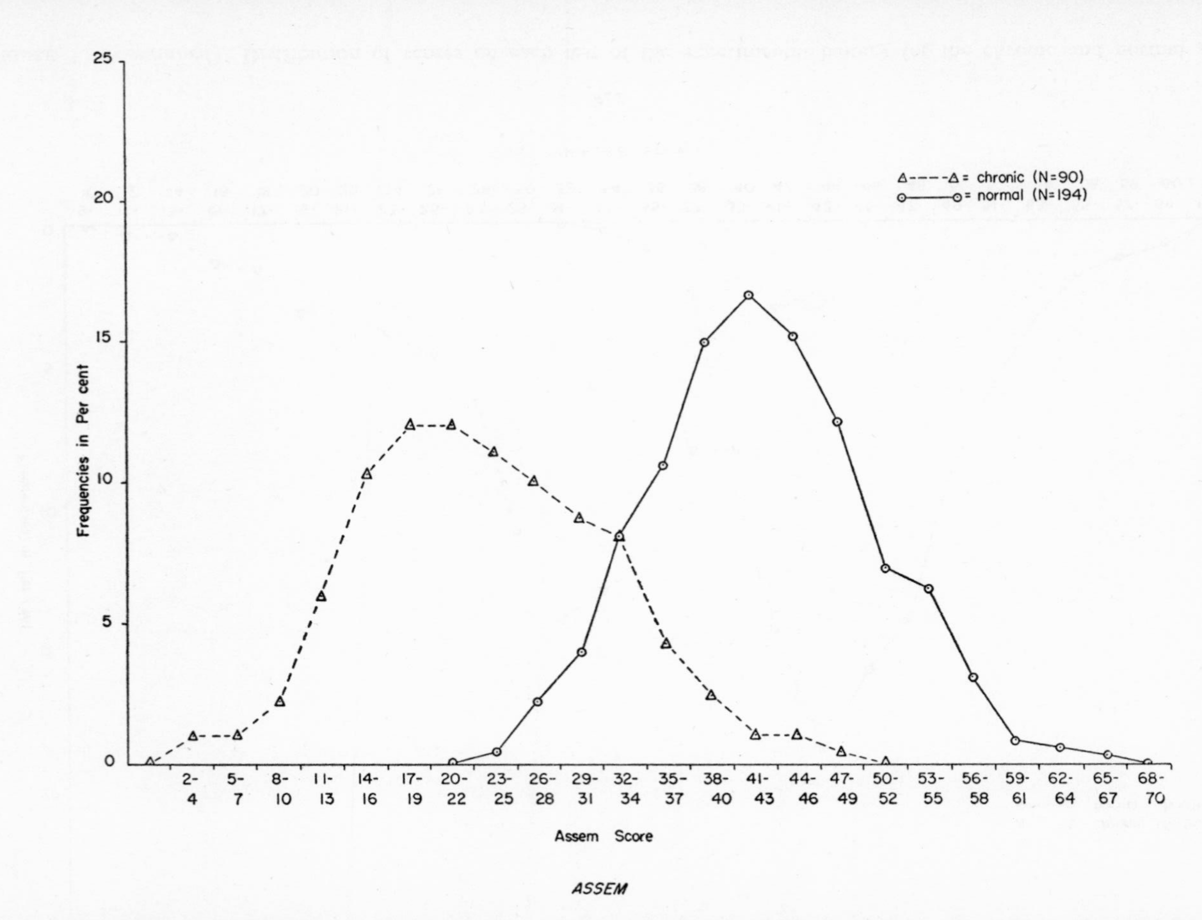

FIGURE 13 (*continued*). Distribution of scores on each test of the experimental battery for the chronic and normal groups.

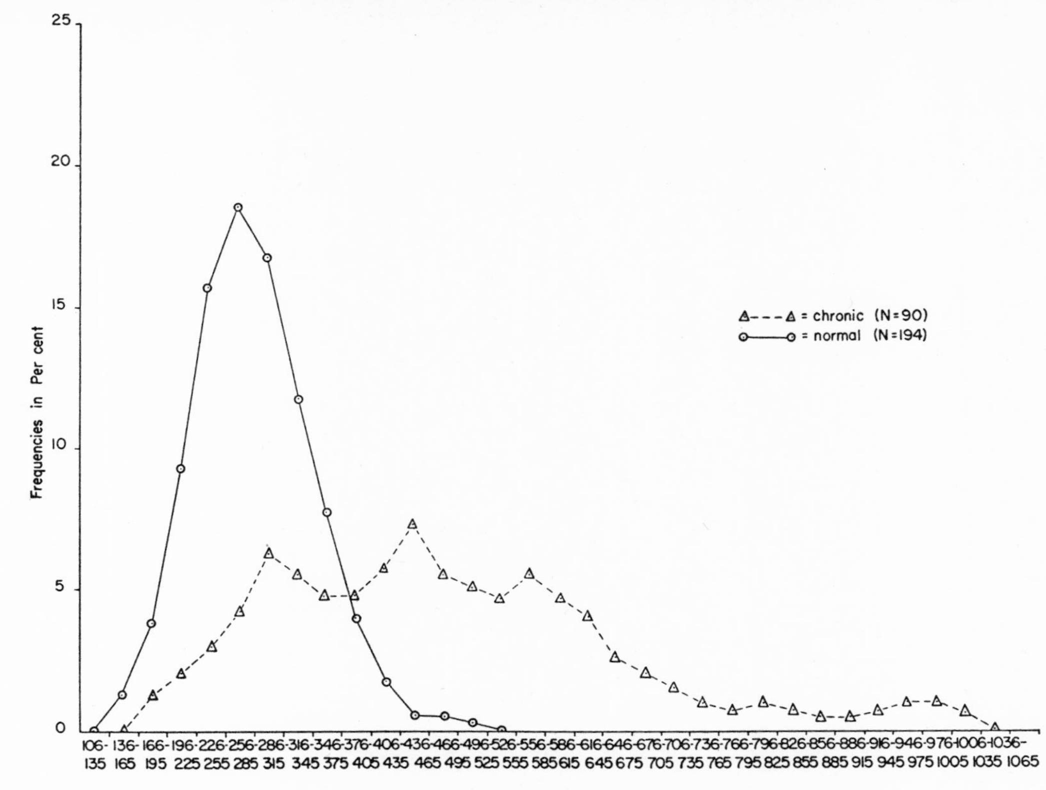

FIGURE 13 (*continued*). Distribution of scores on each test of the experimental battery for the chronic and normal groups.

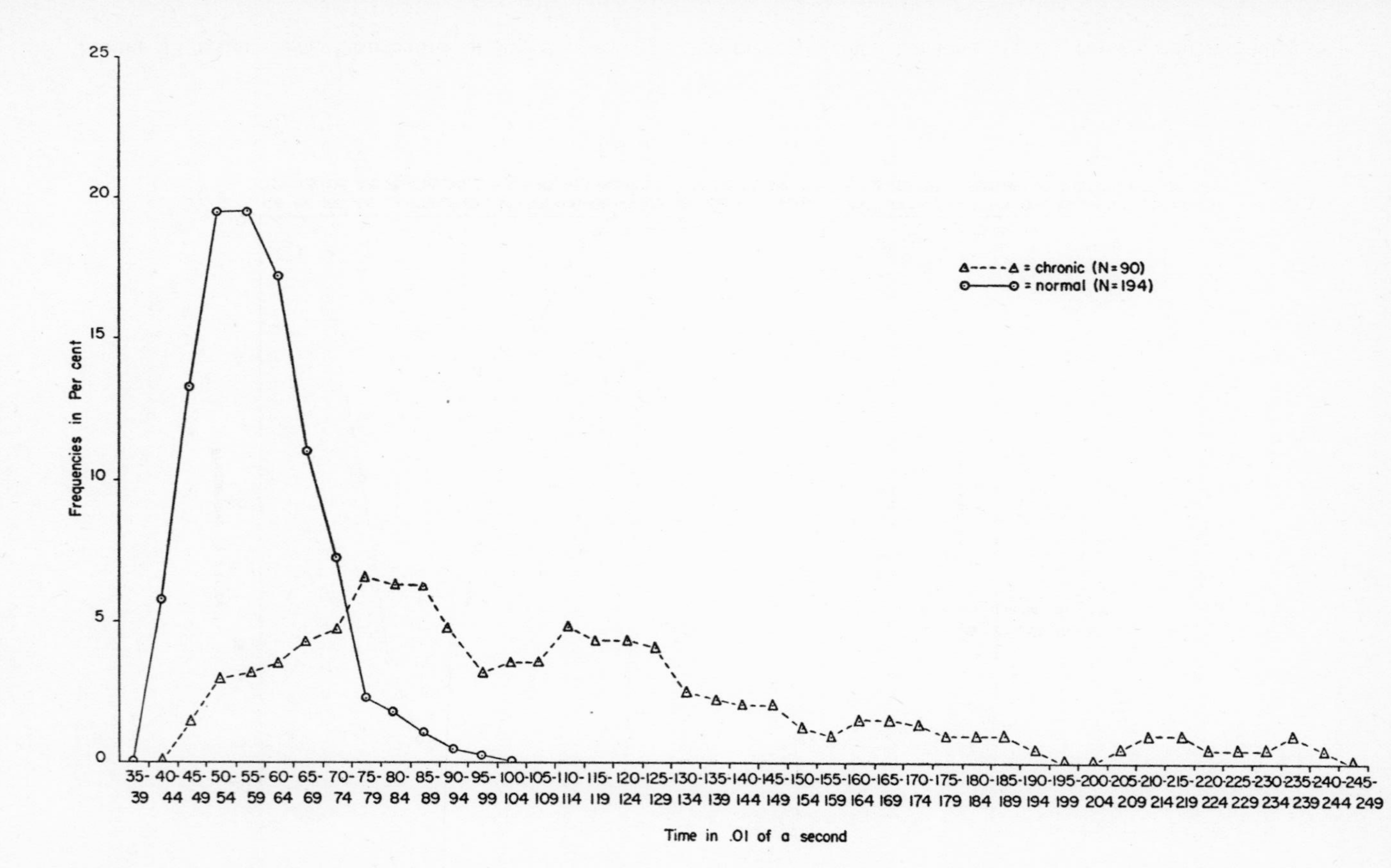

FIGURE 13 (*continued*). Distribution of scores on each test of the experimental battery for the chronic and normal groups.

to which the mean score was related to individual variability, and this relationship was found to be high for the tasks of initiating single movement but in keeping with the normal values for all other tasks. The high correlation existing between the mean and variability measures on the reaction time tasks warns against further analysis by the application of statistical measures which must assume the independence of these measures.

Although the extent to which normal and chronic groups are separated in average, range, and spread of performance is of far greater importance than the degree of overlap visible in the distributions of performance, a question does arise about the group of individuals in the overlapping portions of the curves: who they are and whether they differ in any identifiable way from other members of the chronic group. To attempt an answer at this point would anticipate the use of methods of analysis not yet described and will, therefore, be deferred to a later section of this chapter (see pages 85–87).

THE DISCRIMINATION FACTOR

The comparison of simple and disjunctive reaction time scores yields the following ratios (from Table 15): $RT\ (L)/DRT\ (L) = .73$ and $RT\ (J)/DRT\ (J) = .76$. These values are quite similar to those obtained from performance by the normal group (.69 and .77, respectively) and indicate that when performance on these two types of response is compared, with the simple reaction serving as a base, the element of discrimination constitutes an equal complication for the chronic schizophrenic group and for the normal (see also Table 15). The difference score, arrived at by subtracting the simple reaction time from the disjunctive reaction time, produces larger values for the chronic patients than for the normal group, but does so because of the initially higher numerical values of scores by the chronic group. When the simple and disjunctive responses are taken separately they are certainly found to be slowed in the chronic patient group, but the ratio of "complicated" reaction to simple reaction in the chronic group demonstrates that the defect present appears to reach each type of response in proportionately equal amounts.

TABLE 8. Performance of the chronic group on the tests of fine psychomotor movement (n = 90)

A. Correlation matrix

Tests	*RT (L)*	*RT (J)*	*Tap*	*RLB*	*Assem*	*DRT (L)*	*DRT (J)*
RT (L)	—	.93	.47	.57	.49	.93	.76
RT (J)		—	.52	.19	.17	.86	.86
Tap			—	.57	.59	.38	.51
RLB				—	.68	.50	.56
Assem					—	.46	.57
DRT (L)						—	.79
DRT (J)							—

B. Intercorrelations of key tests

	Tap	*Assem*
RT (L)	.47	.49
Tap		.59

INTERRELATION OF THE TESTS

Table 8 A presents the correlation matrix of the several tests of the experimental battery for the chronic group.[1]

The intercorrelations of the tests are all found to be positive, and are somewhat higher than those obtained from the normal group. The majority of the coefficients show a low or moderate degree of interrelation, but a few rather high correlation coefficients are present. These high coefficients again represent those tasks which were thought to be related to the same essential factors (see pages 14 and 23–24), as was found in the normal group.

The coefficients listed in Table 8 B represent the interrelations of the key measures, or those tests most nearly representing the three basic factors under study. These are taken from Table 8 A, and show some increase in the relationship of tests of the different factors of fine psychomotor ability in performance by this group. These remain at a low-to-moderate level, however, and indicate that the essentially independent nature of the three factors under study is preserved in performance by this psychopathologic group. In general, it appears that there is some heightening of the interrelation in performance on the separate tests among subjects of the chronic group, but that an essentially similar pattern of interrelation holds for both chronic and normal groups.

[1] See footnote 1, page 58.

TABLE 9. Mean scores for chronic group when all patients are ordered in terms of ratings on the psychiatric scale

Group	*n*	*Psychiatric scale*	*RT (L)*	*Tap*	*Assem*	*Psychologic scale*
Least disturbed	30	23	330	15.6	27	361
Moderately disturbed	30	47	390	14.8	27	311
Most disturbed	30	71	627	9.9	20	253

COMPARISON OF SUBGROUPS WITHIN THE CHRONIC GROUP

Several comparisons of subgroups existing within the total chronic group are possible, centering about the degree of behavior disturbance as this is reflected by different methods of classification of the subjects. In making these analyses, only the key measures (*RT* (*L*), *Tap*, and *Assem*) will be included, for purposes of simplicity in presentation. A complete analysis of all test scores has been performed in each instance, and the remaining scores were found to duplicate the trends visible in the key measures.

Gradation by psychiatric scale

Table 9 presents the mean score values on key tests of the experimental battery when the total chronic group is subdivided into the three categories of *least disturbed, moderately disturbed,* and *most disturbed* patients by the method outlined on pages 34–36.

Note that the scores obtained shade off directly, as do the categories of behavior disturbance, reflecting a clear trend toward increased retardation in fine psychomotor performance with increased severity of behavior disorder. Reaction time is lengthened, speed of tapping decreased, and dexterity in assembly decreased. The mean values obtained by use of the psychologic behavior rating scale have also been included in this table to indicate the degree to which this measure is sensitive to the behavior disturbance measured on the psychiatric scale.

Gradation by psychologic scale

Table 10 presents the mean score values on key tests of the experimental battery when the total chronic group is subdivided into the three categories of *least disturbed, moderately disturbed,* and *most disturbed* patients by the method outlined on pages 36–37.

TABLE 10. Mean scores for the chronic group when all patients are ordered in terms of ratings on the psychologic scale

Group	*n*	*Psychologic scale*	*RT (L)*	*Tap*	*Assem*	*Psychiatric scale*
Least disturbed	30	400	302	17.2	30	36
Moderately disturbed	30	325	414	13.1	25	43
Most disturbed	30	200	708	10.1	19	62

Note that in this categorization also the scores obtained shade off, as do the divisions in terms of behavior disturbance, reflecting a clear trend toward increased retardation in fine psychomotor performance with increased severity of behavior disorder. The inclusion of psychiatric scale values serves again as a basis for comparison of the two behavior rating methods.

Gradation by management criteria

Table 11 presents the mean score values on key tests of the experimental battery when the total chronic group is subdivided into the three categories of *least disturbed, moderately disturbed,* and *most disturbed* patients by the method outlined on pages 37–38.

Both psychiatric and psychologic rating scale scores have been included in this table to assist in appraising the extent to which behavior disorder may be identified by hospital management criteria.

Note that once again the scores obtained shade off as do the categories of behavior disturbance, reflecting a clear trend toward increased retardation in fine psychomotor performance with increased severity of behavior disorder.

TABLE 11. Mean scores for the chronic group when all patients are ordered in terms of hospital management criteria

Group	*n*	*Psychiatric scale*	*Psychologic scale*	*RT (L)*	*Tap*	*Assem*
Ordinary ward and working about hospital	24	36	344	344	15.2	27
Ordinary ward, confined	58	48	309	478	13.5	25
Disturbed ward	8	71	199	549	8.4	15

TABLE 12. Mean scores for the chronic group when all patients are ordered in terms of years since first hospitalization

Group	*n*	*Psychiatric scale*	*Psychologic scale*	*RT (L)*	*Tap*	*Assem*
1–5 yrs.	24	31	339	312	17.3	30
6–10 yrs.	26	47	304	530	12.4	24
11–15 yrs.	18	45	319	418	12.7	26
16 yrs. & over	22	50	299	475	12.9	21

Duration of illness

The systematic manner in which scores on psychomotor tests shade off whether the chronic group is subdivided by any of the above three methods of classifying behavior disorder indicates a close degree of relationship of psychomotor performance to clinical status. It may also be instructive to examine this group from the point of view of another more inferential way of estimating the degree of penetrance of the psychosis, by the number of years elapsed since first hospitalization with mental disease. Table 12 presents the mean scores for patients of the chronic group classified in terms of the number of years since first hospitalization (commitment) for mental disease.

It is apparent from the psychiatric and psychologic behavior rating scores included in this table that although a trend exists toward the reflection of greater clinical disturbance with increased years of the duration of illness, this is not as strong as was seen in the gradation of Tables 9, 10, and 11 by current status alone and is subject to some reversals. In a similar way, the psychomotor test scores show only a general tendency in the direction of decreased performance with longer duration of illness, and also exhibit several reversals.

Psychopathologic types

One is tempted to make comparisons among patients of various psychopathologic types within the chronic schizophrenic group, to see whether the same lines drawn by descriptive terminology are duplicated in psychomotor behavior. This temptation should probably be resisted, for present-day psychiatry has broadened the con-

TABLE 13. Mean scores for the chronic group when patients are classified in terms of psychopathology

Group	*n*	*Psychiatric scale*	*Psychologic scale*	*RT (L)*	*Tap*	*Assem*
Hebephrenic-catatonic	43	51	282	527	12.4	24
Paranoid	22	44	343	377	15.5	26

cept of schizophrenia considerably and the Kraepelinian subtypes, never clear-cut or mutually exclusive, are not regarded as separate forms of psychopathology. The patients of the chronic group had all been diagnosed according to the modified Kraepelinian system in use in the hospital, and from these diagnoses perhaps one justifiable stratification may be made. There appears to be a tendency for chronic schizophrenic patients to fall into two biologic as well as psychologic types (57, 58), one group principally characterized by delusion (paranoid) and one by the presence of deterioration (hebephrenic-catatonic). The chronic group has been subdivided on this basis, and the behavior scale and key psychomotor scores for these groupings are given in Table 13.

This subdivision, unlike previous ones, does not include the entire group since only those cases with clear-cut symptomatology could be classified; these constituted about two-thirds of the total chronic group. The prior assumption would be that the deteriorated group represents a core group with a deeper penetration of the psychosis. Note that the behavior scale scores tend to bear this out, although the distinction between groups is not extreme. Similarly, the key psychomotor scores show greater retardation in the hebephrenic-catatonic group, although here, too, the distinction between the groups is not extreme.

Sex, age, education, health, and body type

The demonstration in previous analyses of this group that much of the variance in psychomotor performance is assumed by psychosis and its gradations makes it appear that analysis in terms of other factors is limited at the outset. Even so, the question may be raised as to the relationship of such performance to major categories descriptive of the group. Table 14 presents the mean scores on the behavior rating scales and key psychomotor tests when the

TABLE 14. Mean scores for the chronic group when all patients are classified in terms of sex, age, education, health, and body type

Group	*n*	*Psychiatric scale*	*Psychologic scale*	*RT (L)*	*Tap*	*Assem*
1. Sex						
male	45	46	300	428	14.0	24
female	45	46	317	470	13.0	25
2. Age						
20–44	51	51	304	460	12.7	25
45–69	39	42	314	434	14.5	24
3. Education						
0–8 yrs.	54	47	298	462	13.4	23
9 yrs. & over	36	47	320	429	13.6	26
4. Health						
good	66	49	308	459	13.4	25
fair	24	41	309	420	13.6	25
5. Body type						
pyknic	16	48	320	542	11.7	27
asthenic	33	48	293	414	14.0	25
athletic	39	25	318	447	13.9	23
dysplastic	2	41	286	312	11.5	27

chronic group is divided on the basis of sex, age, education, health, and body type.

Sex: The behavior rating scores show the groups to be about equal in symptomatic expression, and key psychomotor scores are also approximate. Such deviations as can be seen are in the direction observed among normal subjects.

Age: Subdividing the total group into a younger and an older group, the behavior scales indicate slightly greater symptomatic disturbance in the younger group, and this trend is borne out in the *RT (L)* and *Tap* scores, although it is slightly reversed for *Assem.*

Education: Number of years of schooling furnishes a rough index of intellectual ability, and since complete intelligence measurements were not available for this group, a division of the group on the basis of educational achievement may furnish some idea of the interrelation of this factor with psychomotor performance. The behavior scales indicate that when the total group is divided into those with 8 years or less of formal education and those with 9 years or more, symptomatic expression is approximately the same, with some advantage (fewer symptoms) for the group with greater education. Psychomotor scores are also very similar, with a slight favoring (higher scores) of those with 9 or more years' schooling.

Health: The periodic physical examination of patients in the chronic group requires a statement by the examining physician of whether their general physical health is good, fair, or bad. Since the category for bad health was not used for any of the patients of this group, a classification of patients as in good health or fair health has been made. Scores on the behavior scales are similar for these two groups, with a minor advantage for the *fair* group. Psychomotor scores are also very similar, with a minor advantage for the *fair* group.

Body Type: Patients of the chronic group were classified into the four Kretschmer types, but one category, the dysplastic, received only 2 cases, and so actually there is but a three-way division of the cases. It is difficult to detect any systematic trends among the behavior and psychomotor scores for this classification; even the different behavior ratings are in minor disagreement.

These various methods of making subdistinctions in the degree of psychosis present in the chronic group make it clear that fine psychomotor measurement methods, in addition to distinguishing the group as a whole from normal individuals, accurately parallel finer gradations of the clinical condition of the patients in this group. This is best shown by the rating methods which make the most adequate division of the group on the basis of behavior disorder, and may also be seen in the close parallel between psychomotor performance and other stratifications of the total group.

THE DISCRIMINATION FACTOR WITHIN THE CHRONIC GROUP

The methods for describing gradations within the chronic group having been explained, it would now be of interest to examine the interrelation of symptom categories with the factor of discrimination within the chronic group. As a representative example, Table 15 presents the simple and disjunctive reaction time values when the total group is subdivided on the basis of psychiatric ratings, as explained on pages 34–36.

Note that the ratios $RT\ (L)/DRT\ (L)$ and $RT\ (J)/DRT\ (J)$ remain essentially unchanged despite difference scores of increas-

TABLE 15. Simple and disjunctive reaction time means for the chronic group

Group	*n*	*RT (L)*	*DRT (L)*	*Diff-erence*	*RT (L)/ DRT (L)*	*RT (J)*	*DRT (J)*	*Diff-erence*	*RT (J)/ DRT (J)*
Total	90	449	611	162	.73	89.0	117.0	28.0	.76
Subgroups*									
least	30	330	467	137	.73	69.3	86.6	17.3	.81
mod.	30	390	542	152	.74	80.5	106.8	26.3	.76
most	30	627	822	195	.77	117.0	155.9	38.9	.75

*Psychiatric scale subgroups: least disturbed, moderately disturbed, and most disturbed.

ing magnitude as we go from least to most disturbed behavior subgroups. It appears that an equal difficulty is presented to least disturbed, moderately disturbed, and most disturbed patients by the added complication of making this discriminative response.

PATIENTS IN THE "OVERLAP" GROUP

A question arises about the nature of the patients whose performance was found to overlap that of the normal group; i.e., in what way do they differ from other members of the chronic group? Actually, the finding of distributions which overlap on measures of some biologic or psychologic characteristic is to be expected (e.g., the height or I.Q. of different racial groups), and only the wide degree of separation of chronic and normal groups in this instance calls special attention to the fact that portions of their distribution curves overlap. It must be remembered that we are not examining a pathology *per se,* which might be expected to make a complete separation of the pathologic from the normal, but rather the faulty performance of a basic human characteristic which may relate to the pathology of behavior.

In terms of the test score achieved, the number of patients from the chronic group who score higher than the lowest normal is rather large and includes roughly half the total group for each test. If we contrast these patients with those who scored completely below the normal range we may learn more of the relation between behavior disorder and fine psychomotor performance. Table 16 presents the psychiatric and psychologic rating scale scores for patients in these two groups, together with the classification of the patient as a hospital management problem and the number of years since his first commitment to a mental hospital.

TABLE 16. Psychiatric and psychologic rating scores, hospital management criteria, and duration of illness for patients in the "overlap," and "non-overlap" subgroups of the chronic group

				Hospital management criteria			Duration of illness			
				Ordinary ward						
Test and subgroup	*n*	*Psychiatric scale*	*Psychologic scale*	Working	Confined	*Disturbed ward*	*1–5 yrs.*	*6–10 yrs.*	*11–15 yrs.*	*16 yrs. & over*
RT (L)										
Overlap	30	36.2	369	11	17	2	11	8	5	6
Non-overlap	60	52.1	276	13	41	6	13	18	13	16
Tap										
Overlap	41	38.5	354	14	27	0	14	11	7	9
Non-overlap	49	54.5	270	10	31	8	10	15	11	13
Assem										
Overlap	42	39.4	354	14	27	1	12	14	8	8
Non-overlap	48	53.2	268	10	31	7	12	12	10	14

Inspection of this table shows that for each of the key tests, ratings by psychiatric and psychologic scales indicate that patients falling in the "overlap" group show less symptomatic deviation from the normal than do those falling outside this range. In terms of hospital management criteria the picture is less clear, but does indicate that fewer patients of the "overlap" groups need be placed on disturbed wards. Similarly, fewer patients in the "overlap" groups have had long periods of hospitalization for mental disorder. The groups do not differ appreciably on the basis of age or sex. The general pattern observed is one of less behavior deviation by those patients falling in the "overlap" groups. A further retrospective analysis of the case histories of those individuals falling in the "overlap" groups might help to describe the way in which they differ from other members of the chronic group. The diagnoses are firm, however, to the extent that all patients of this group have had a minimal hospitalization of at least 1 year, with an average of over 9 years, and to establish a relation to the hospital course of each patient would require a detailed analysis of descriptive material beyond the scope of this study, for there are no objective diagnostic tests on which to base the diagnosis or status of schizophrenic patients other than the description of the behavioral life history of the patient.

One would also like to know whether the "overlap" group consists of the same individuals from one test to another. The correlation coefficient for the total group answers this, in part, and indicates that the different tests have a low-to-moderate relationship in the group as a whole, and that to the extent of the intercorrelation some of the same individuals would be found in the "overlap" group on each test. Previous analyses on each test also show that "better" performance on fine psychomotor tasks is definitely associated with those individuals who depart the least from normality. One would expect, then, to find that the "overlap" groups, consisting of somewhat less deviant individuals (as shown in Table 16), would be likely to score in the upper end of their distributions most consistently. This is found to be true by actual count, and a degree of correspondence is found ranging between 57 and 80 per cent, depending upon which test is used as a reference point.

SAMPLE CHRONIC PATIENT PERFORMANCE

In Chapter 4 a sample individual record selected from the normal group was given to aid in forming an idea of what normal performance on the test battery looks like. The record given below was similarly selected to serve as a comparable sample of typical performance by a member of the chronic patient group:

TESTS

Trials	*RT (L)*	*RT (J)*	*Tap*	*RLB*	*Assem*	*DRT (L)*	*DRT (J)*
1	496	86	11	39	19	753	116
2	336	77	12			547	97
3	226	64	13			430	93
4	255	68	15			989	138
5	737	111	13			410	79
6	491	90	14			793	132
7	776	120	13			780	118
8	779	73	14			420	87
9	240	68	14			652	105
10	367	81	13			988	137
11	740	65					
12	198	66					
13	264	64					
14	341	70					
15	279	73					
16	561	99					
17	438	83					
18	287	74					
19	716	75					
20	445	87					
Mean	448.6	79.7	13.2	39	19	676.2	110.0
σ	198.2	15.2	1.08			209.7	20.2

Subject No. 69 is a female, 47 years of age, formerly a grocery store clerk and newspaper correspondent. She is a high school graduate and unmarried. She has been hospitalized with a diagnosis of dementia praecox, hebephrenia for 21 years without remission. Primary symptoms: She hallucinates, shows defective judgment, and is agitated and fearful at times. Mental content: She hears voices saying that she is going to be killed and she feels strange sensations, probably electricity, in her body. She is sociable, quiet, and cooperative.

Note the large increase over the normal in scatter, or intra-individual variability, in the performance of tasks with multiple trials, particularly those of the reaction time factor. Compare this with the normal record on page 61.

SUMMARY OF FINDINGS ON THE CHRONIC GROUP

The pattern of fine psychomotor performance by the chronic group on tests of the experimental battery is in striking contrast to that given by the normal group. Their records are clearly of a retarded nature on all tests, expressing a general reduction of fine psychomotor ability.

The form and rate of improved performance as a result of practice at the tasks was found to be quite regular and to resemble clearly the patterns set by the normal group. There was a somewhat greater irregularity present in the learning curves for the chronic patients, but the course of improvement with practice was seen to follow nearly identically that of the normal group. Most of the gains were made early in the practice series, and all responses reached a level of relative stability within the period of observation. It is apparent that familiarity with the tasks and learning factors have about the same influence upon the performance of this group as on that of normal individuals, and that different processes of learning do not account for the differences later found in average performance.

The scores obtained by the chronic group on the post-practice measures on each test of the battery have been collected and presented in both tabular and graphic form (Table 7; Figure 13). They present a picture of markedly reduced level of average performance, lowered range of scores and increased variability of response. The principal comparison of performance by the chronic and normal groups, that of average levels of response, is summarized in Figure 14.

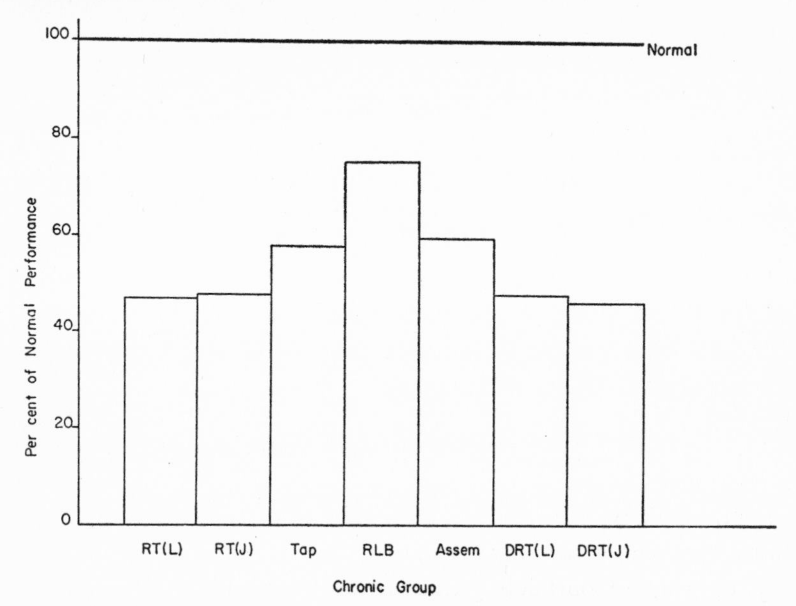

FIGURE 14. Average performance on each test of the experimental battery by the chronic group, expressed as a percentage of normal performance.

In this diagram, performance by the chronic group on each test has been expressed as a percentage of normal performance. The differences between groups are readily apparent, scores by the chronic group being roughly only 50 per cent of the normal value. The chronic group also differs from the normal in its pattern of inter-individual variability. Although some increase in variability is present in performance on all tests of the battery, it is the extraordinary increase in variability on the tests of reaction time which shows the most definite departure from the distribution of scores in the normal group.

The introduction of a discrimination situation in reaction time, which has been described as resulting in an increase in the time of reaction in the normal group, was also found to increase the time of reaction among the chronic patients. This increase was seen to be directly proportional to speed in the simple reaction time situation, however, and indicates that the additional complication of making a discriminative reaction is much the same for the chronic group as for the normal.

The interrelation of tests in the battery was found to be somewhat intensified, particularly among those tests which relate to the same basic factor, but indicates that despite some increase in the correlation of key tests of the three essential factors under study, these tests do not coalesce in the presence of strong psychopathology but continue to sample more or less independent elements of psychomotor ability.

Several methods were devised for dividing the patients of the chronic group into smaller subgroups so that comparisons might be made of the least disturbed, moderately disturbed, and most disturbed patients of the total group. Scores on the fine psychomotor tests were found to parallel such classifications closely, and indicate that performance on tests of the experimental battery both reflects gradations of the symptomatic disorder in behavior and distinguishes the chronic group as a whole from the normal. When the group is divided on the basis of the duration of illness and psychopathologic type, only minor trends in clinical or symptomatologic status were seen to accompany these characteristics, and, in a similar way, only minor paralleling trends were found in the psychomotor performance for such grouping. An analysis of the group on the basis of sex, age, education, health and body type failed to indicate significant trends either in terms of clinical status or psychomotor performance.

Further inquiry into those chronic patients whose psychomotor performance scores overlap the lowest scores of the normal group shows that these individuals are characterized by less deviation from normal behavior than is true of patients whose scores fall completely below the normal range. A count of the individual patients found in the portion of the chronic group distributions overlapping the lowest normal score on the several different tests of the battery showed that between 57 and 80 per cent of the same individuals are represented, depending upon which test is used as reference.

In brief, a pattern of fine psychomotor performance was found for the chronic schizophrenic group which, though similar to the normal in the learning and stabilizing of response, showed a dramatically different range and level of average performance. Gradations of symptomatic disorder within this group further systematically indicated that the tests of the experimental battery definitely and consistently parallel the degree of behavior disorder present.

CHAPTER 6

STUDIES WITH PSEUDONEUROTIC SCHIZOPHRENES AND NEUROTICS

(SUBACUTE BEHAVIOR DISORDERS)

THE test procedures that were followed with the subacute group were identical with those described in Chapter 4 for the normal group.

PRACTICE

The learning curves of performance by the subacute group on tests of the experimental battery show a close similarity to those describing performance by the normal group. Progress is orderly, and a relative stability of response is reached after the same number of practice trials found sufficient for stabilization in the normal. The learning curves of the normal group have been repeated in the figures exemplifying learning by the subacute group in order to facilitate comparison (Figures 15–17).

Reaction time (lift)

The practice curve of the performance by the subacute group for lift reaction time is given in Figure 15.

Very little reduction in the time required for response is noticeable upon repeated performance, and a slight irregularity of the practice curve may be noted, particularly in the first trials at the second sitting (trials 21–25).

Note that performance by the two groups is more alike on the early trials than on those following. This tendency may be seen even more clearly in the *RT* (*J*) measure.

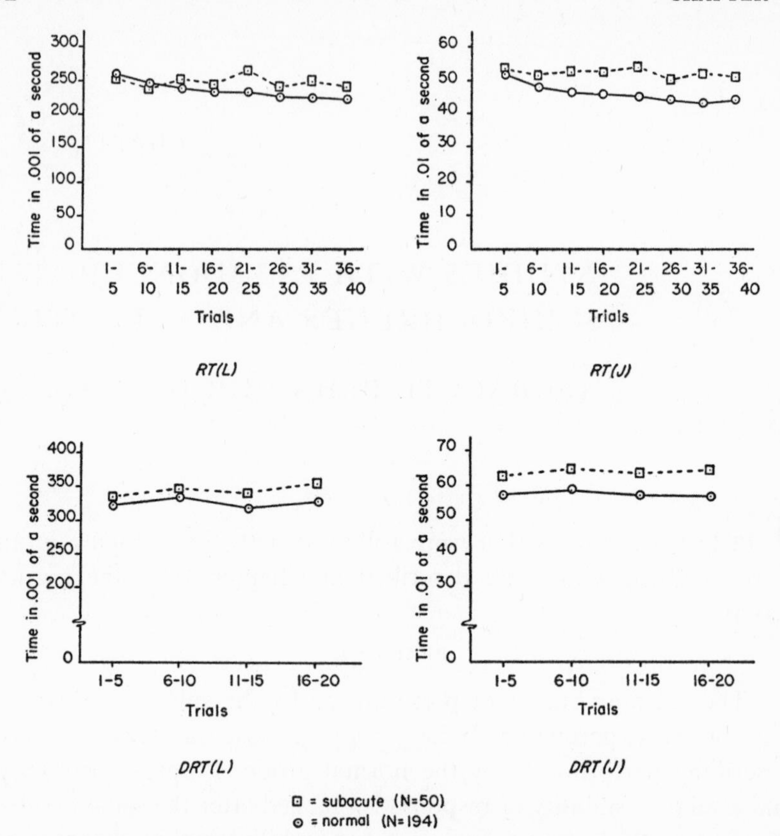

FIGURE 15. Learning curves on the tests of reaction time for the subacute and normal groups. Each point plotted represents the mean of 5 trials.

Reaction time (jump)

The practice curve of the subacute group for performance on the jump reaction time task is given in Figure 15. A slight reduction in the time required for response may be seen to occur, but it is very slight. Most of the improvement in performance takes place during the first 15 trials. Some irregularity of the practice curve is also apparent on this task, particularly at the beginning of the second sitting (trials 21–25).

Although the initial performance of the normal and subacute groups is of about the same time value, a greater reduction in the time required for response is visible in performance by the normal group at the end of the series.

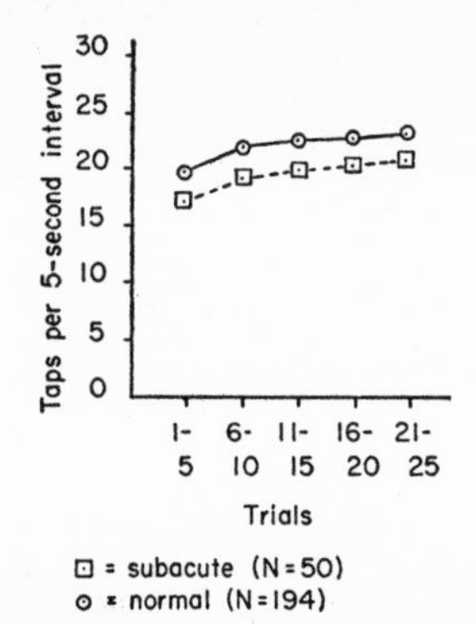

FIGURE 16. Learning curves on the tapping test for the subacute and normal groups. Each point plotted represents the mean of 5 trials.

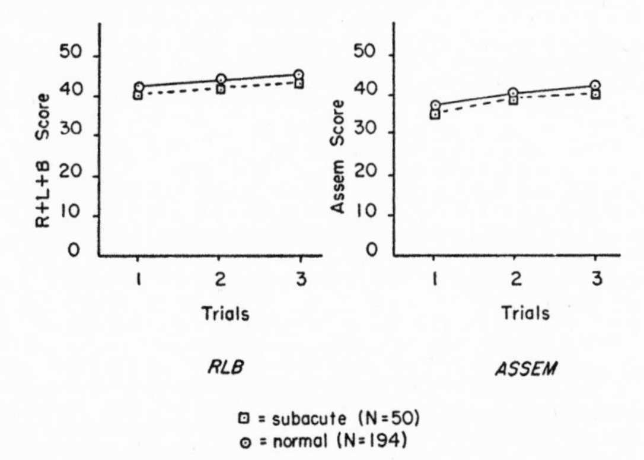

FIGURE 17. Learning curves on the dexterity tests for the subacute and normal groups. Each point plotted represents 1 trial.

Tapping speed

The practice curve of the subacute group for performance on the tapping task is shown in Figure 16.

A gradual growth function indicates an improvement in performance with practice, most of which occurs during the first 10 trials, and a continued slight gain is visible throughout the series.

Dexterity

RIGHT HAND, LEFT HAND, AND BOTH HANDS. The practice curve for the subacute group on the score which represents summed performance by the right hand and left hand separately and the two hands used together is shown in Figure 17.

Some improvement in performance may be seen on each trial. As in the normal group, most of this gain occurs on the second practice trial.

ASSEMBLY. The practice curve for the subacute group performance on the assembly task is shown in Figure 17. A definite improvement in performance may be seen on each trial, most of which occurs on the second trial.

Disjunctive reaction time (lift)

The practice curve for the subacute group on the task requiring a discrimination reaction time (the lift response) is shown in Figure 15. It appears that practice has very little effect upon this response, and that continued performance tends to lengthen very slightly, rather than shorten, the latency of response.

Disjunctive reaction time (jump)

The practice curve for the subacute group on discrimination reaction time (the jump response) is shown in Figure 15. Repetition seems to exert little influence on this response, performance tending to be much the same throughout the series observed.

An inspection of these learning curves reveals a close similarity of performance by the subacute group to that of the normal. The shape of the curves is strikingly similar for performance by these two groups on any given task, and a level of approximate stability is reached after the same number of practice trials in each. This is true for both individual tasks and for the series as a whole. There is a minor trend for performance of the two groups to be more alike initially on tests of reaction time than they appear later in the practice series; but there is no indication of this in performance on other tests of the battery. It appears that a level of stability in response is achieved on all tasks of the battery within the period of observation which approximates that which would be obtained with extended practice, but the same exception to this general statement must be made for the measures of dexterity as was taken for performance by the normal group; namely, that this response did not stabilize within the practice allowed and that a longer practice period would be desirable (see page 48).

TABLE 17. Mean scores on tests of the experimental battery for the subacute and total normal groups and for a normal comparison group with a similar age range and average

Test		*Subacute group* ($n = 50$)	*Total normal group* ($n = 194$)	*Normal group** *(matched for age)* ($n = 99$)
RT (L)	M	222	209	201
	σ	47.4	34.7	27.0
RT (J)	M	49.4	44.0	40.7
	σ	8.7	7.5	4.8
Tap	M	20.5	22.6	23.7
	σ	3.3	3.3	2.5
RLB	M	43.6	45.6	46.7
	σ	4.0	4.6	4.3
Assem	M	40.3	41.2	44.0
	σ	6.0	6.4	5.7
DRT (L)	M	324	303	281
	σ	83.7	86.6	51.1
DRT (J)	M	62.6	57.2	52.7
	σ	13.1	12.6	6.3

*These scores are based directly on the scores for age decades 20–29 and 30–39 of Table 4 B.

TEST SCORES AND THEIR DISTRIBUTION

The psychomotor performance scores for the subacute group on each test of the experimental battery have been computed on the basis of post-practice performance, and Table 17 presents the means and standard deviations for all tests.

Both the scores for the total normal group and for a normal group of the nearest approximate age range and average have been included in this table to aid in the direct comparison with performance by the subacute group. The correction for age is made necessary by the relative youth of the subacute group, with an average age of 30.3 years and a range of 14.8–49.0. The normal subjects nearest this age average and range who have been employed as the most similar comparison group are the complete 20–29 and 30–39 age decade groups of the total normal sample; that is, all subjects from the total normal sample between 20–39 years of age. This normal subgroup is made up of 99 subjects, 57 males and 42 females, with an average age of 30.5 years and an age range of 20.7–39.7 years.

The distribution of scores obtained on each of the tests is presented graphically in Figure 18, and the distribution curves of the normal subgroup of similar age average and range have been added to this table to facilitate direct comparison.[1]

A small but consistent trend toward unusually expanded variability may be noted in the performance of the subacute group on those tasks relating to initiating a single movement, but the curves of distribution are generally gaussian in form.

COMPARISON OF TEST SCORES WITH THE NORMAL GROUP

Small but consistent differences may be seen to exist between the post-practice indicators of psychomotor performance by the subacute group and those of the total normal group. This may be seen in the learning curves for the two groups (Figures 15–17) and in the mean scores achieved by each of these groups (Table 17). When a necessary correction for age is made, by comparing the performance of the subacute group with that of a normal subgroup made up of subjects of their approximate age, the contrast between performance by subacute patients and the normal is emphasized even more. Although these departures from normal are not as striking as the major discrepancies of performance observed between the normal and chronic patient groups, they are not inconsequential and all are found to differ significantly from normal performance ($p > .01$) when examined by Fisher's "t" test.

In general, there is an obvious similarity of performance by this group to that of the normal, far greater than that observed in the chronic group. Small and consistent differences from the norm may be noted in average performance, and to some extent also in the range and variability of response. In each instance the difference is in the direction of slightly retarded performance by the subacute group, indicating less rapid performance on all tests of the experimental battery. The increase in variability on those tasks relating to the initiating of single responses has already been mentioned, and is in the direction of greater inter-individual variability of response for the subacute group. The scores of the subacute patients appear to reflect, in lesser degree, most of the same alterations in fine psychomotor performance previously seen in greater magnitude

[1] See footnote, page 52.

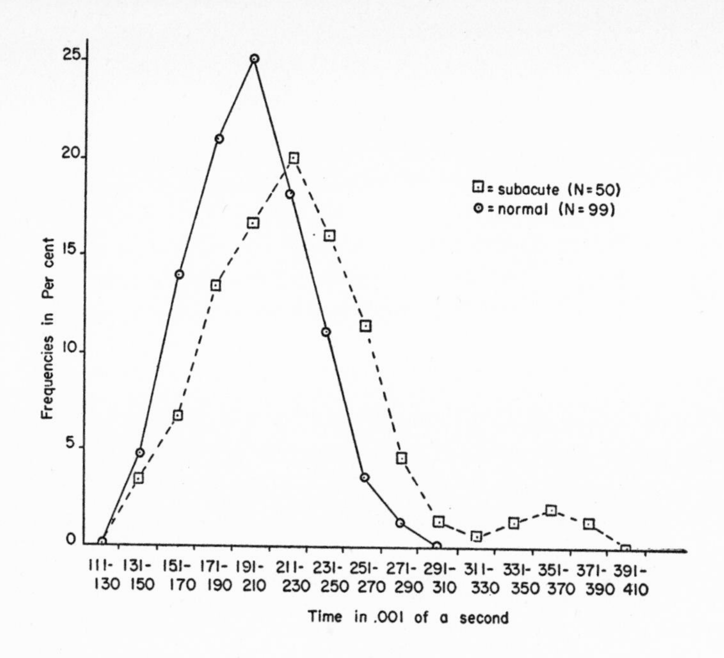

RT(L)

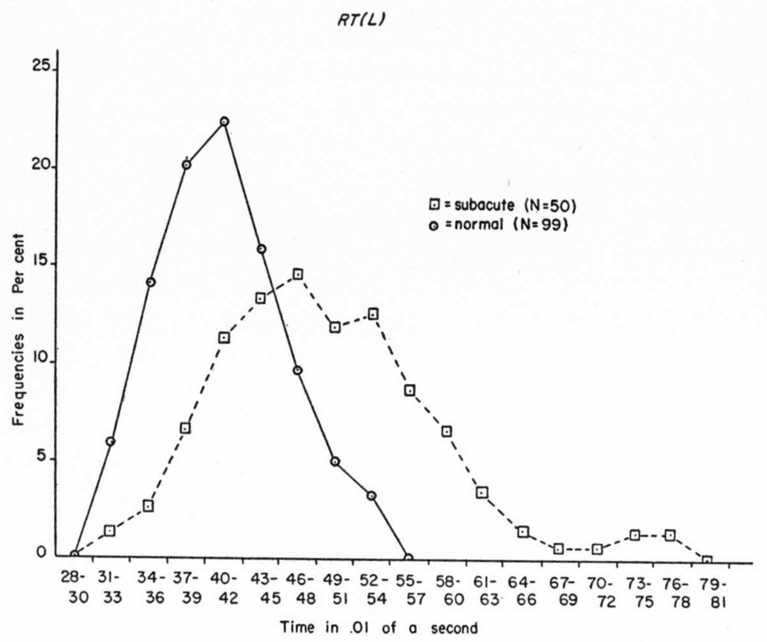

RT(J)

FIGURE 18. Distribution of scores on each test of the experimental battery for the subacute and normal groups.

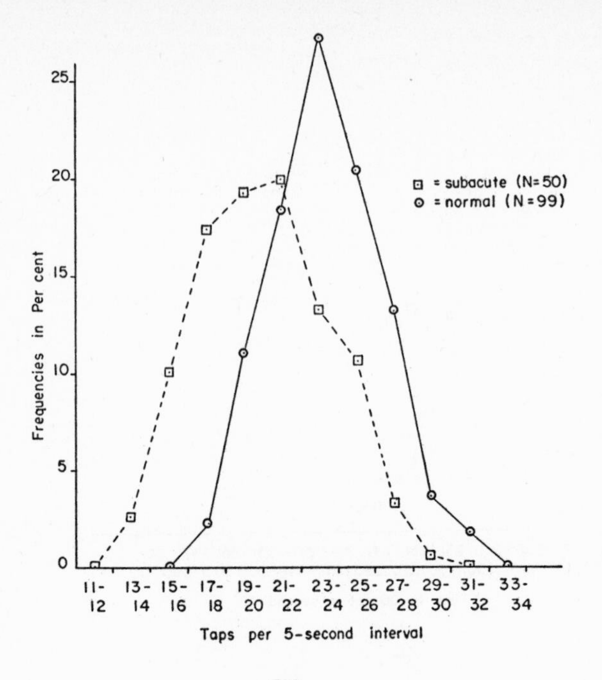

TAP

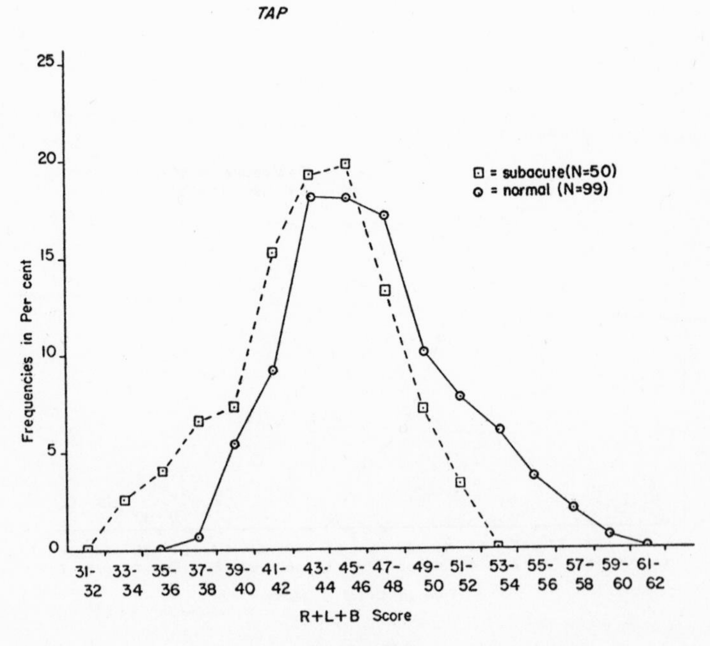

RLB

FIGURE 18 (*continued*). Distribution of scores on each test of the experimental battery for the subacute and normal groups.

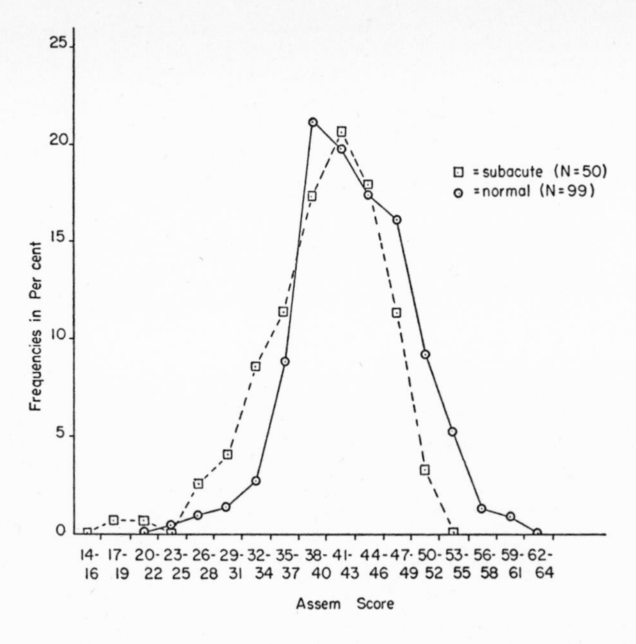

ASSEM

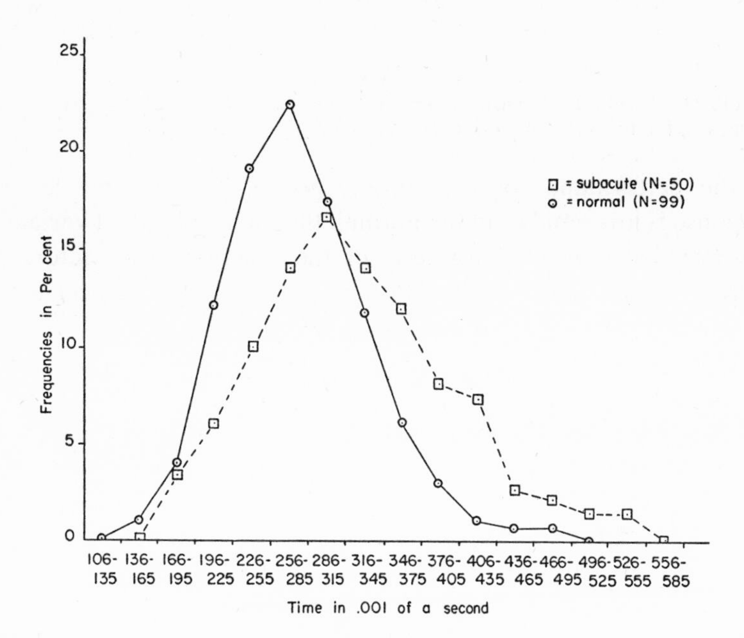

DRT(L)

FIGURE 18 (*continued*). Distribution of scores on each test of the experimental battery for the subacute and normal groups.

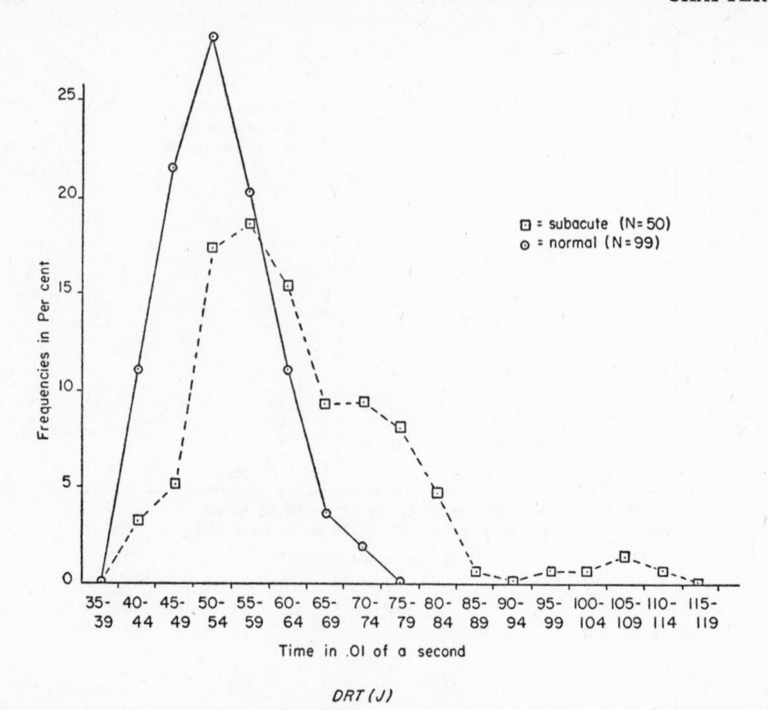

FIGURE 18 (*continued*). Distribution of scores on each test of the experimental battery for the subacute and normal groups.

in the performance of the chronic group. The average level of response is less rapid than the normal, the inter-individual variability is somewhat expanded for tests of the reaction time factor, and there are even some changes in the range of response which illustrate a shift to a lower order of response.

THE DISCRIMINATION FACTOR

A comparison of simple and disjunctive reaction time for the subacute group yields the following ratios (from Table 20): *RT (L)/DRT (L)* = .69 and *RT (J)/DRT (J)* = .79. Here again, as was noted for the chronic group, the values obtained are very similar to those of normal subjects (.69 and .77, respectively), indicating that when performance on these two types of response are compared with the simple reaction, the element of discrimination appears to constitute the same degree of complication for the subacute group as it does for the normal.

TABLE 18. Performance of the subacute group on the tests of fine psychomotor movement (n = 50)

A. Correlation matrix

Tests	*RT (L)*	*RT (J)*	*Tap*	*RLB*	*Assem*	*DRT (L)*	*DRT (J)*
RT (L)	—	.75	.23	.29	.35	.81	.70
RT (J)		—	.48	.17	.22	.67	.85
Tap			—	.17	.12	.26	.32
RLB				—	.63	.21	.19
Assem					—	.33	.26
DRT (L)						—	.83
DRT (J)							—

B. Intercorrelations of key tests

	Tap	*Assem*
RT (L)	.23	.35
Tap		.12

INTERRELATION OF THE TESTS

Table 18 A presents the correlation matrix of performance on the several tasks of the experimental battery for the subacute group.[1]

All of the intercorrelations obtained are positive. Those coefficients which show the interrelation of the several tests of the reaction time factor are slightly higher than the corresponding coefficients in the normal group, but the interrelation of the two dexterity tasks is much the same as that found for the normal.

The coefficients listed in Table 18 B represent the intercorrelations of the key measures of the test battery, those most nearly representing the three basic factors under study. These are drawn from Table 18 A, and show rather low correlations among the key tests, indicating a slightly more independent nature of the three factors under study than was found in the intercorrelations of the normal group.

In general, the correlations obtained with this group show a pattern of interrelation much like that found for the normal group, with the exception of a somewhat intensified relation of the several tests of reaction time, and a slightly lower relation among the key tests of the battery.

[1] See footnote 1, page 58.

TABLE 19. Mean scores on tests of the experimental battery for the total subacute group, the neurotic and pseudoneurotic schizophrenic subgroups, and a normal comparison group with a similar age range and average

Test		*Neurotic* ($n = 23$)	*Pseudoneurotic schizophrenic* ($n = 27$)	*Total subacute* ($n = 50$)	*Normal* ($n = 99$)
RT (L)	M	200	241	222	201
	σ	31.1	50.8	47.4	27.0
RT (J)	M	45.9	52.3	49.4	40.7
	σ	6.6	9.2	8.7	4.8
Tap	M	20.7	20.4	20.5	23.7
	σ	3.7	2.9	3.3	2.5
RLB	M	44.3	43.1	43.6	46.7
	σ	3.6	4.3	4.0	4.3
Assem	M	41.7	39.0	40.3	44.0
	σ	4.3	7.0	6.0	5.7
DRT (L)	M	287	356	324	281
	σ	57.2	89.2	83.7	51.1
DRT (J)	M	57.2	67.1	62.6	52.7
	σ	7.6	15.1	13.1	6.3

COMPARISON OF SUBGROUPS WITHIN THE SUBACUTE GROUP

One major subdivision of the subacute group has been anticipated; it is made possible by separating members of the total group into the two categories of neurotic and pseudoneurotic schizophrenic individuals, as described on pages 39–42. This gradation is one of both quantity and quality of symptoms expressed. Table 19 presents the means and standard deviations computed for performance by these two subgroups on tasks of the experimental battery, together with scores of the total subacute group and the scores of a comparison group of normal subjects of similar age range and average.[1]

When the mean scores of the neurotic and pseudoneurotic schizophrenic subgroups are compared, a consistent difference in performance is apparent, in which the pseudoneurotic schizophrenes show a greater retardation in psychomotor test performance than do neurotics. A trend is also visible toward a greater expansion of variability on the tasks of initiating a single response for the pseudoneurotic schizophrenes than for the neurotics.

When the mean scores of these two subgroups are further com-

[1] See footnote to Table 17, page 95.

TABLE 20. Simple and disjunctive reaction time means for the subacute group

Group	*n*	*RT (L)*	*DRT (L)*	*Diff-erence*	*RT (L)/ DRT (L)*	*RT (J)*	*DRT (J)*	*Diff-erence*	*RT (J)/ DRT (J)*
Subacute	50	222	324	102	.69	49.4	62.6	13.2	.79
Neurotic	23	200	287	87	.70	45.9	57.2	11.3	.80
Pseudo-neur. schiz.	27	241	356	115	.68	52.3	67.1	14.8	.78

pared with those of normal individuals of comparable age range and average, it becomes clear that performance by the neurotic group resembles that of the normal subjects much more closely than does performance by the pseudoneurotic schizophrenic group. Although performance by both subgroups falls somewhat short of the standard set by the normal group, the performance of the pseudoneurotic schizophrenic group may be seen to differ more from the normal and to deviate more consistently in the direction of slowed response. Most of the deviation from normal by the subacute group as a whole appears, therefore, to be based upon the performance of the pseudoneurotic schizophrenic subjects.

A further inquiry into the ratio of simple to disjunctive reaction time on the basis of this subdivision of the subacute group in terms of diagnosis is given in Table 20.

The ratios of *RT (L)/DRT (L)* and *RT (J)/DRT (J)* for the neurotic and pseudoneurotic schizophrenic subgroups are found to be very similar to those of the normal group (which are .69 and .77, respectively), and the degree of complication imposed by the discrimination situation appears to be the same for normals, neurotics, and pseudoneurotic schizophrenes.

SAMPLE SUBACUTE PATIENT PERFORMANCE

The detailed record of performance by an individual from the subacute group given below may help to make clear the type of performance obtained from members of this group on tests of the experimental battery:

Subject No. 824 is a female, 29 years of age, housewife, married, has three children. She is a grammar school graduate. She is being treated in an out-patient psychiatric clinic and has a diagnosis of *pseudoneurotic schizophrenia.* Primary symptoms: She is depressed, restless, hypochon-

			Tests				
Trials	*RT (L)*	*RT (J)*	*Tap*	*RLB*	*Assem*	*DRT (L)*	*DRT (J)*
1	402	80	16	46	40	341	84
2	228	55	18			346	89
3	293	65	19			266	75
4	196	56	19			372	100
5	220	58	18			259	58
6	243	66	17			358	88
7	205	64	18			253	63
8	221	60	19			405	72
9	257	68	18			378	82
10	243	69	19			306	94
11	211	66					
12	212	54					
13	228	68					
14	220	73					
15	229	61					
16	296	84					
17	252	75					
18	242	70					
19	265	71					
20	251	66					
Mean	245.7	66.4	18.1	46	40	328.4	80.5
σ	44.2	7.7	.95			51.5	12.7

driacal and suffers anxiety attacks. Mental content: She feels unloved, has lost faith in God, feels nothing has any meaning but death, feels hate for all others, and at times is not sure who she is.

Note the increase in intra-individual variability above that of the normal, as well as the increases in mean score for those tasks with multiple trials. Compare this with the normal record given on page 61.

SUMMARY OF FINDINGS ON THE SUBACUTE GROUP

The pattern of fine psychomotor performance by the subacute group shows an over-all similarity to that of the normal group, but clearly reflects small and consistent retardations on all tests of the battery.

The rate of improved performance as a result of practice is regular and parallels the normal learning curves on all tasks. A slight increase in irregularity is visible in the learning curves for tests of the reaction time factor, but the course of improvement is almost identical with that of the normal group. Most of the gains on repeated performance were made early in the practice series, and

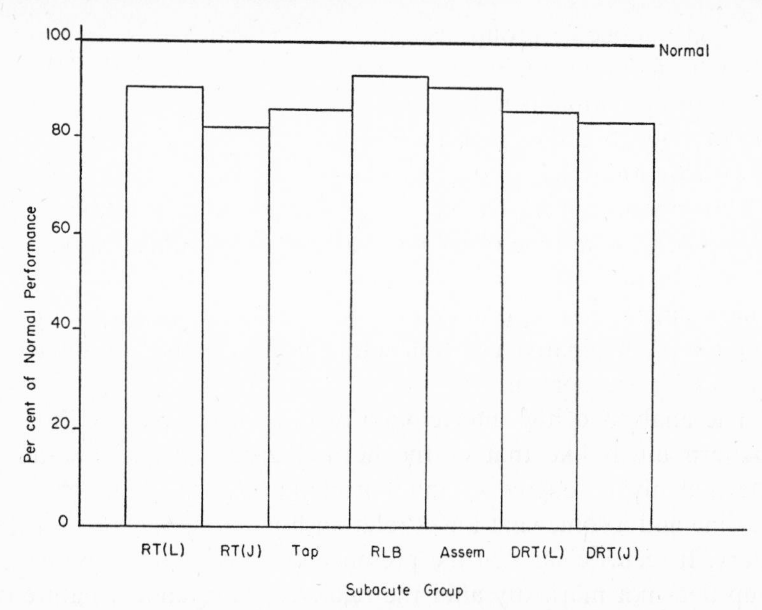

FIGURE 19. Average performance on each test of the experimental battery by the subacute group, expressed as a percentage of normal performance.

all reached a level of general stability within the period of observation. The close similarity of the learning curves of this group to that of the normal indicates that no major differences in the learning processes occur for these two groups.

The scores obtained by the subacute group on the post-practice measures on each test of the battery have been collected and are presented in both tabular and graphic form (Table 17; Figure 18). They present a picture of minor retardation in average performance on all tests, together with some lowering of the range of response and a tendency toward increased inter-individual variability of response on the tests of reaction time. The principal comparison of performance by the subacute group and a group of normal subjects of comparable age range and average, that of average levels of response, is summarized in Figure 19.

In this diagram, performance by the subacute group on each test has been expressed as a percentage of normal performance. The differences between average scores for the two groups are apparent, the scores of the subacute group being roughly 88 per cent of the normal value, and are significant at the .01 level of confidence. The subacute group also differs somewhat from the normal in its pattern of inter-individual variability. The distribution of scores for the group is similar to the normal for the tests of tapping speed and dexterity, but shows increases over the normal on the several tests of reaction time.

Performance in the discrimination reaction time situation shows that the increase in time of response needed to meet this elementary difficulty is proportionately about the same as that required by normal subjects. It appears that the additional complication of making a discriminative reaction is much the same for the subacute group as for the normal.

The analysis of the interrelation of tests of the battery showed a pattern much like that of the normal group but containing a somewhat higher degree of intercorrelation for the tests of reaction time and a somewhat lower relationship among key tests of the battery. It seems clear that the presence of psychopathology in this group does not markedly alter the relatively independent nature of the elements of psychomotor ability under study.

A gradation of behavior disorder within the subacute group by diagnostic classification as neurotic or pseudoneurotic schizophrenic reveals some retardation in performance by each group. The degree of retardation observed is greater for the pseudoneurotic schizophrenic group than for the neurotic group. A strong influence in the deviation of the total subacute group from the normal may, therefore, be attributed to those subjects classified as pseudoneurotic schizophrenics.

In brief, a pattern of fine psychomotor performance was found for the subacute group which, though very similar to the normal in the learning and stabilizing of response, showed small but significant and consistent retardations when compared with normal response. A gradation of the degree of behavior disorder within the subacute group by diagnostic classification as neurotic or pseudoneurotic schizophrenic indicated a relatively more retarded performance by the pseudoneurotic schizophrenic patients.

PART III

Discussion

CHAPTER 7

RESULTS OF THIS EXPERIMENT

THE comparison of performance by normal and psychopathologic subjects taking part in this experiment demonstrates, with clarity, that a psychomotor defect does indeed characterize states of disordered behavior; at least, it does so for those of the type under study, which represent a major proportion of known sorts of behavioral abnormality. This defect has been found to be of varying degree depending upon the type and amount of behavioral deviation present, but it presents a consistent over-all pattern of disturbed psychomotor function which accompanies the symptomatic expression of mental disease. It must be emphasized that the term *psychomotor* refers to voluntary action systems of the individual, with all that this connotes, and that whatever eventual relation may prove to exist between these and structural neurologic components of the motor system of the body, the present discussion necessarily relates only to the individual responding in accordance with the instructions of the experimenter.

It has been stated several times, in the course of presentation, that as full an understanding as is possible of the course of fine psychomotor performance of the normal person on these tests is a prerequisite for the adequate comparison of performance by psychopathologic groups. Now that the records of groups selected on different bases are to be compared, the need for this understanding may be more directly appreciated. This is particularly true for the observations made upon the practice or learning series by the experimental groups, for several facts of importance must be drawn from a study of these curves, even though they include many more scores than those upon which intergroup comparisons have been based.

In comparing the performances of different sorts of individuals on psychomotor tests, we wish to know, as we do when employing any type of test procedure, something about the homogeneity of performance by a wide range of subjects, to what extent practice or familiarity with the task results in improved performance, and what are the approximate limits of performance. These questions become of increased significance when groups are to be compared in which there is any reason to suspect, on prior grounds, that they will approach the task in a different way. All studies including a voluntary performance of any sort by mental patients contain this element of doubt and call for a close inspection of the approach made to the task. For this reason a considerable emphasis has been given to the acquisition process of the normal, chronic, and subacute groups of this study. By repeating the learning curve for the normal group on the graphs describing learning by the psychopathologic groups, this active process may be visually compared. The curves reflect a high degree of similarity in acquisition between the normal group and the chronic group on each of the tasks included in the experimental battery (Figures 10–12), and the same is true of performance by the subacute group (Figures 15–17). The performance of all three groups is summarized in Figure 20. The normal group shows very little improvement with practice on tasks of initiating movement, and the psychopathologic groups show even less. All groups describe most similar curves of performance on other tasks. What may we infer from this which will aid the comparison of groups on the indicators chosen? First, that since the learning curves of the different experimental groups follow very similar courses and appear to reach levels of stability approximating those which would be reached with extended practice, we may compare the performance of different groups without concern that we are intersecting different processes at a point arbitrarily chosen by the performance of the normal group alone. That is to say, both the normal and psychopathologic groups appear to benefit in the same manner by repeated performance, and therefore comparison of their relative performance at any given point tends to exert no favor for either group. Another inference may be justified relative to the motivational status of the groups. Any great difference in the motivation and effort put into performance at these tasks might be

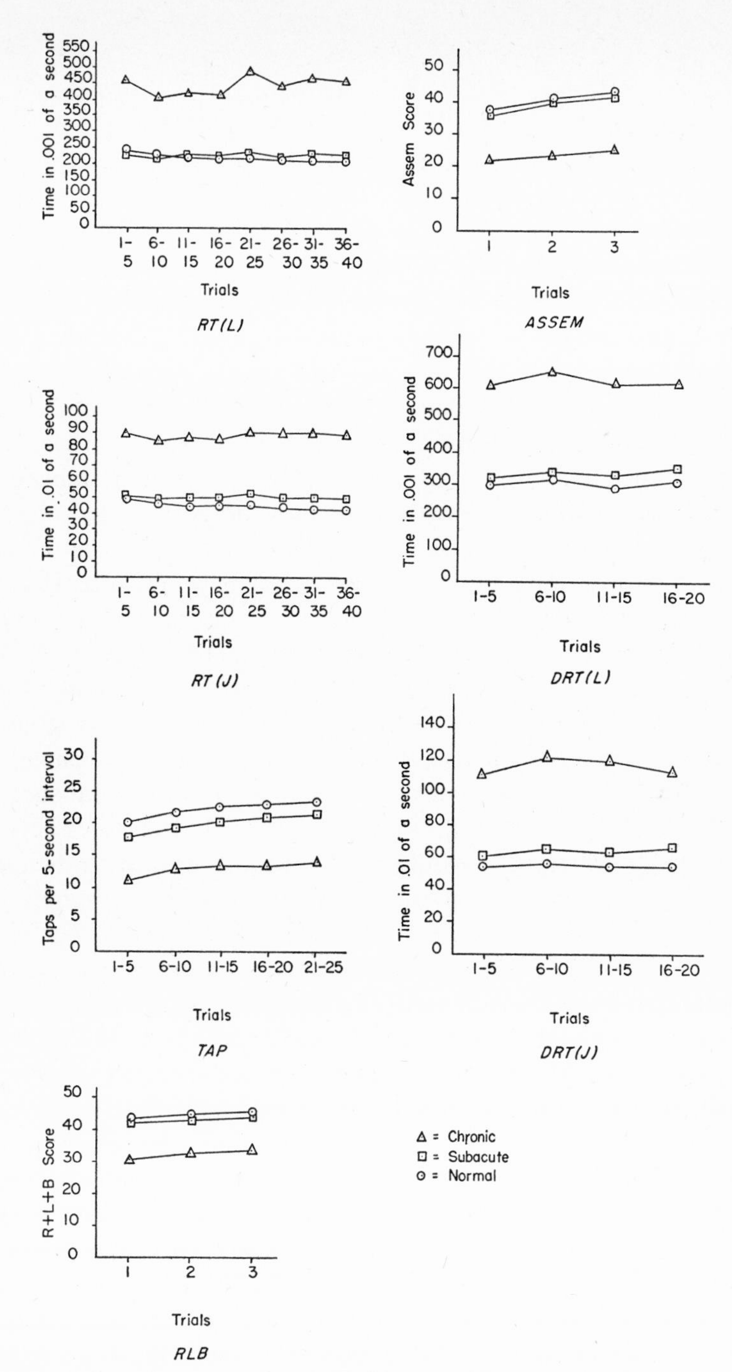

FIGURE 20. Learning curve on each of the tests of fine psychomotor performance for the normal, chronic, and subacute groups.

expected to reveal itself in altering the curves of performance through the learning period. A lack of motivation or a tendency toward increasing or quickly dissipated effort should manifest itself in the rate of acquisition and improvement in performance consequent upon practice. Whatever discrepancies may exist in original levels of effort, the curves obtained do not appear to indicate any difference in the rates of acquisition of the movements called for by these tests. The orderly performance by the psychopathologic groups indicates, in fact, that continued effort was expressed throughout all test performances. From these facts it would appear that reasonable comparisons may be made between the performance of the experimental groups, using responses given after a stable level has been reached as the basis for the indicator.

The heart of the comparison between performance by the normal and psychopathologic groups has thus been made by comparing the responses of each group following a sufficient period of stabilizing practice. The contrast in psychomotor performance between the chronic schizophrenes and normal persons is clearly delineated and consistent in its appearance. Table 7 shows that the chronic schizophrenic group is clearly less rapid in psychomotor response when compared with the normal on all individual subtests of the experimental battery. Further, Tables 9, 10, and 11 make it clear that when varying degrees of behavior disorder are distinguished within the group of chronic schizophrenes, psychomotor performance by these groups reflects the degree of disturbance directly, with greater degrees of retardation becoming apparent as the symptomatic expression of psychotic behavior is increased. Tables 12 and 13 show, also, that the relation of the amount of behavior deviation to such factors as duration of illness and type of psychopathology are faithfully reflected by performance on the psychomotor battery.

The degree of retardation in psychomotor response is considerably less for the subacute group than for the chronic schizophrenic group, as, indeed, is the degree of behavior disorder. When a diagnostic distinction is made, among members of this group, between the neurotic and the presumably more morbid pseudoneurotic schizophrenic patients, the performance of pseudoneurotic schizophrenes may be seen to account for most of the retardation in

TABLE 21. Comparison of mean performance for the normal, subacute, and chronic groups on tests of fine psychomotor movement

	CHRONIC			SUBACUTE		NORMAL
Test	*Most disturbed* ($n = 30$)	*Moderately disturbed* ($n = 30$)	*Least disturbed* ($n = 30$)	*Pseudo-neurotic schiz.* ($n = 27$)	*Neurotic* ($n = 23$)	*Normal* ($n = 194$)
RT (L)	627	390	330	241	200	209
RT (J)	112.4	80.5	69.4	52.3	45.9	44.0
Tap	9.9	14.8	15.6	20.4	20.7	22.6
RLB	29.8	35.0	35.8	43.1	44.3	45.6
Assem	20.0	26.8	27.0	39.0	41.7	41.2
DRT (L)	822	542	467	356	287	303
DRT (J)	155.9	106.8	86.7	67.1	57.2	57.2

psychomotor performance visible in the total subacute group, while the responses of neurotic subjects differ little from those of the normal (Tables 17 and 19).

To return to the ordering of the experimental groups in descriptive terms suggested in Chapter 3, a rough continuum is formed by the subjects of this experiment, ranging from those exemplifying the most severely disturbed behavior through moderate disorder and to the normal in this way:

(Chronic)			(Subacute)		(Normal)
I	II	III	PNS	N	Norm

I represents the most disturbed, II the moderately disturbed, and III the least disturbed subclass of the chronic group as established by psychiatric ratings (pages 34–36). Table 21 presents the data on psychomotor performance by the different groups and subgroups of subjects in a form suitable for making this comparison. The relative levels of average performance on key tests of the battery by the same subject groupings are also shown in Figure 21.

The relation of speed in fine psychomotor performance to this gradation by external criteria is direct and of considerable subtlety. As presupposed, the steps in this ordering are undoubtedly unequal (p. 42) and the approximations of the continuum somewhat rough, but the paralleling of the degree of behavior disorder as indicated by psychiatric diagnosis and rating methods by the performance on psychomotor tasks of the experimental battery is most striking and provides grounds for further speculation as to why this should be so.

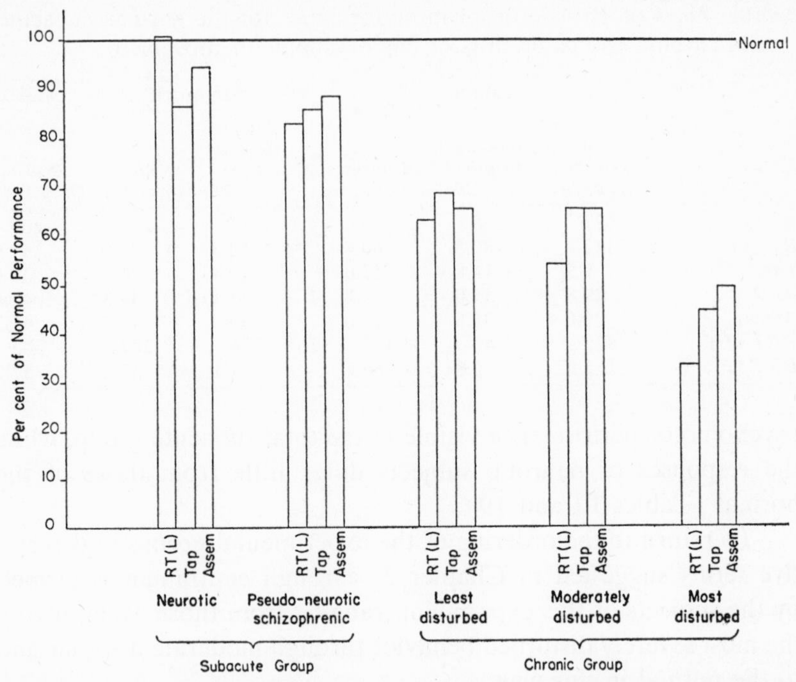

FIGURE 21. Average performance on key tests of the experimental battery by the subacute and chronic subgroups, expressed as a percentage of normal performance.

It is apparent from these data that the experimental groups differ on individual subtests, as well as on the battery as a whole, and this fact presents a point of interest, for it is clear from the performance of both normal subjects and patients that low to moderate relationships exist between different subtests of the experimental battery (Tables 6, 8, and 18). It would appear, then, that whatever factor lies behind these alterations in schizophrenic subjects, it acts in a pervasive way, affecting simultaneously types of psychomotor performance which are to a large extent distinct and distinguishably different types of activity. One of the purposes in introducing the correlational matrix of performance for each of the subject groups was to observe the degree of interrelation existing in each group individually so that the effect of the presence of behavior disorder on this interrelation might be observed. The thought was that increasing degrees of behavior disorder might, in fact, be accompanied by an increasing of the strength of the interrelation of the separate subtests, and that as one proceeded from normal through subacute to chronic groups, a systematic heightening of correlations might take place, indicating a "regression" effect or reduction to a single factor. This idea was based on the notion that if a strong factor was present which affected the individual as a whole (e.g., withdrawal) this would color all performance simultaneously and perhaps upset the pattern of interrelation normally found in such performance. This does not prove to be the case, however, and except for a minor trend in the direction of heightened intercorrelation of different tests for a single factor one cannot say that the presence of behavior disorder has in any way distorted or seriously affected the usual interrelation of performance on various psychomotor tasks from that seen in the normal.

Another clearly evident trend which emerges from contrasting the psychomotor performance of the three experimental groups is the tendency toward increased variability of response in tasks of initiating movement as compared with performance on other tasks. If performance on all tasks had shown this inflation of variability, there would appear to be a factor producing variation among schizophrenic patients of equal or even basic importance to the mean differences which exist, but although some increase in variability is apparent in performance at other tasks it is not greatly magnified or in any sense extraordinary. It was originally intended to express the *intra-individual* variability of each subject on each test in a single score and to average these scores for experimental groups in a way similar to that employed by King (63) in treating intra-individual variability on intelligence tests. This type of measure gives an indication of the spread of scores on different test trials made by an individual about his own mean score, and extends our grasp of variation in performance from what may be seen in the group situation (inter-individual variability) to the individual. This plan was not put into effect, for by inspection alone it was apparent that the different groups do indeed differ in their intra-individual variability of response, and that in the tests of the reaction time factor in particular this is directly related to differences found in mean performance. The sample individual records given with each patient group give an illustration of this effect (pages

61, 87–88, and 103–104). Other studies of this element in the psychomotor performance of individuals with a behavior disorder are now under way which present a more hopeful basis for its analysis by (*a*) especially selecting tests for this type of study which are not characterized by strong inter-individual variability, and (*b*) emphasizing repeated studies of psychomotor performance by the same individuals at different test sittings, separated by days, weeks, etc. The extraordinary *inter-individual* spread of responses obtained in all instances of testing the chronic group on tasks of initiating movement are amply clear to the eye in the distributions given in Figure 13. Furthermore, the tendency of the subacute group to show an attenuated form of such expanded group variability is also distinct in Figure 18. It seems clear that the timing regulation of responses of this sort is affected by the presence of behavior disorder and that this is probably related to the changes in mean score on such tests.

Within this type of task, initiating single responses, it is interesting to note that the inclusion of a discrimination factor, the making of an elementary decision, does not seem to constitute any greater difficulty for the subject with behavior disorder than for normal persons, though such an interpretation has been placed on previous similar experimental findings. Viewed in terms of the absolute time difference between simple and disjunctive responses, there would appear to be increasing difficulty of initiating action as one passes from the normal through mild and moderately disturbed behavior to the category of most disturbed behavior, since the difference scores between simple and choice response increase regularly with this progression. That this represents increased difficulty in the more complex situation is obviously only an apparent effect, however, for the ratio of simple to disjunctive response, using each group's simple response measure as its best denominator, consistently fails to indicate any increase in the simple-to-disjunctive ratio which would indicate an increased slowness in discrimination response in the groups more strongly affected by behavior disorder (Tables 5, 15, and 20). Tangentially, this also appears to offer some further assurance that a reasonably comparable level of attention was maintained in all groups, even in those cases most disturbed in their behavior, since no haphazardness of response or sluggishness in decision is apparent on the basis of this type of performance.

It must be borne in mind that the particular tests selected for inclusion in the present battery are only samples of psychomotor activity, and are restricted even further to samples of fine psychomotor movements. The factors singled out by prior analysis were intended to serve as a guide to experimentation only, and the indicators employed should by no means be considered to be the best or only approach to the psychomotor aspects of mental disease. They appear to be well suited to the task of differentiating the performance of chronic schizophrenes from that of the normal, and to be effective as well in differentiating the performance of persons with subacute behavior disorders. In distinguishing normal from subacute cases the task might be much assisted by the employment of psychomotor methods and tests more nearly tailored to performance by the normal and near-normal individual. For example, the pursuit rotor task or samples of tracking behavior, although they appear to be too difficult to apply to cases with severe behavior disorder, might serve best to differentiate the performance of normal and near-normal groups. Many different tasks, representative of the multiple facets of human psychomotor function, must be employed with patients suffering from all types of behavior disorder before it will be possible to gain a secure grasp on the interaction of mental disease and psychomotility as a broad function of the individual.

Having stressed the fact that the tests used in this study are but samples of a broader realm of psychomotor function, perhaps some remarks about details of the particular tests which were employed may be appended, to describe more fully the observations made on their use.

Of the several tests included in the battery, those which center about the initiating of a single response appear to be the most powerful in the differentiation of psychopathologic groups and in reflecting subtle differences between classes of subjects. This may be a consequence of the penetration of the disease process to involve this basic type of psychomotor movement, or the result of the highly precise measures of time recording made possible by the method. The high positive correlation found to exist at all times and in all groups between lift reaction time and jump reaction time indicates that the instrumentally simpler method of measuring jump reaction time, though somewhat less sensitive than the fast component of commencing action (lift), is quite adequate to the measurement of the gross disruption of function seen in the patient groups studied. The employment of the two methods together, as described on pages 16–18, makes it possible to observe directly the two components of a given response to a stimulus signal: lifting the finger (*RT* (*L*)), and cross-and-press (*RT* (*J*)) response. These paired observations allow us to note, for example, that in the discrimination situation both types of measures of the ensuing response are slowed from the rates established for simple response, with about the same proportional delay in each, being slightly greater for the measures of lift reaction time.

The tapping test, too, has been seen to serve well in the differentiation of psychopathologic groups. Although it has not been mentioned in the various sections describing the results obtained with the tapping test on each experimental group, a detailed analysis of the pattern and tempo of tapping responses has been made. The instrument employed marked on a moving tape the onset of the start signal, each response of the subject, time and the end of the test period (stop signal). From these graphic records it is possible to analyze the performance of individuals and groups in order to determine whether the pattern of response or its tempo was related to total tapping performance within the test periods. It was thought that different groups of subjects might present different methods of response, e.g., one might begin slowly and accelerate, another begin rapidly and then slow, etc. In actual performance, few such differences are found to occur between individuals, and groups are not differentiable at all on this basis. For the most part, a rate is begun and slightly improved in the first second of performance, remaining constant for the balance of the test period. This is true of all groups studied in this experiment. Since this characteristic does not appear to succeed in distinguishing among groups of this sort, the apparatus might be much less complex, with a simple impulse counter replacing the recording element.

The dexterity tasks employed appear to involve more in the way of an organization of effort, since they are sustained activities requiring a certain degree of sustained control. The performance of all groups makes it clear that more practice than was allowed is really required to achieve stabilization of response on this type of task. A very simple test, its principal value appears to lie in the possibility of contrasting simple and organized movements within the same test and thus offering an index of the relation between speed and control.

Several attributes of psychomotor measurement methods, such as those described here, are of value in their experimental use in the investigation of mental disease. These, of course, do not in any way improve the power of the tests to differentiate between groups of individuals, but prove to be of real assistance in planning and executing research in areas where they are found to be definitive. I refer to such qualities as their simplicity, reliability, objectivity, and the fact that they may be repeated at will, once a training series is complete and stable performance achieved. The fact that we may repeat a measure of performance without introducing contaminating factors because it *is* being repeated is of definite assistance in appraising the status of an individual subject at any given moment. Psychologists have not been as fortunate in the application of their measures of human function as, say, the chemist or physiologist, for prior experience alone serves to influence performance on so many of our measurement techniques. Methods which prove themselves to have differentiating power in the analysis of psychologic function and which also possess the virtues of objectivity, reliability, and repeatability are thus doubly welcome inclusions in the psychologic laboratory.

In seeking an explanation of the limitations of psychomotor performance demonstrated in this experiment, perhaps the first idea to come to mind is that the indications of slowed response are reflections of the altered motivational status said to characterize mental patients in general and schizophrenic patients in particular. The impairment in average level of psychomotor response may be simply the symptomatic reflection of a disturbed mental state. Schizophrenic patients, for example, are clinically characterized by a withdrawal from contact with the environment to a subjective life preoccupied with its own problems, and are less responsive to ordinary external pressures than would normally be expected. Such patients may similarly tend toward reduced participation in the psychomotor test situation, with a consequent loss in quality of performance.

Despite the common-sense appeal of such an explanation of the phenomena observed, it is found, on further analysis, to be unsatisfactory for several reasons and to fail to account for certain of the data obtained. It is based on a logical construct, that of motivation, which is itself inferred from visible action. It is clear, however, that many different known variables may achieve an end result of lessened psychomotor output, such as age, sex, anoxia, fatigue, the presence of drugs, and so on, and that no certain one-to-one relationship exists between motivational factors in the individual and final psychomotor output. Several qualities of psychomotor performance, as well as its average or optimal levels, should also be directly affected by a state of lowered motivation in the test subjects. The learning curves, for example, would be expected to be of a different order in groups of subjects of widely different motivational strength. Data from the present experiment make it clear, however, that the learning process appears to be most similar in psychomotor performance by patients classified clinically as having a severe behavior disorder, those with a milder behavior disorder, and normal individuals. A motivational or attitudinal factor strong enough to result in the group differences observed in average performance might also be expected to alter the balance of intercorrelations found among such test performance by normal individuals, uncomplicated by behavior disorder. The data of this experiment do not seem to reflect the entry of any strong ordering influence, however, in the interrelation of tests of psychomotor ability by the groups suffering from partial or severe behavior disorder. One might further expect strong motivational differences in patients with a mental disease to manifest themselves by exhibiting a relatively greater degree of impairment in complex tasks than in simple ones. The single contrast of this type in the present experiment, that of simple and disjunctive reaction time, did not indicate a relatively greater degree of psychomotor impairment on the more complex task. To these facts from the present investigation we might add the relevant observation that a state of lowered participation by reason of lessened motivation might be expected also to blunt performance on other psychologic tests, particularly those requiring much in the way of patience, fine discrimination, and persistence. The mass of evidence obtained on psychopathologic patients indicates, however, that although a certain minor degree of defect is often present in performance on sensory, intellectual, and perceptual tasks in the behavior disorders, the relative defect in psychomotor test performance is far more marked and of greater consistency. The largest single population studied by both detailed psychomotor and non-psychomotor tests illustrates this differential in performance specifically (68, 69).

Although the discrepancies cited do not suffice to indicate, with positiveness, that an explanation in terms of motivational status may not account for the data at hand, the inconsistencies which have been noted make it appear that a simple explanation of psychic withdrawal or symptomatologic reflection of one kind or another is not altogether satisfactory in accounting for the data observed or in helping to gain an understanding of the processes involved in the production of the observed phenomena. It would be premature to attempt to rule out the possible influence of such psychologic factors from the situation at our present rudimentary stage of empiric and analytic knowledge of psychomotor response among the mentally ill. At the same time, if the action of motivational influences operates in a manner similar to that known to obtain in normal human psychology and among the lower animals—and there is no reason to expect it to be otherwise—then the trends and tendencies noted above which characterize the psychomotor performance of the mentally ill are not easily understood on a simple basis of inadequate application to the task at hand. A more basic cause may be in operation to produce the observed differences in performance, extending beyond the reflection of psychologic attitudes characteristic of the disorder.

To form a more general hypothesis about the nature of the disturbances observed in psychomotor performance by the psychopathologic groups of this experiment, it will first be necessary to relate these findings to those reported by other investigators who have performed experiments bearing on the relation of psychomotor performance to mental disease. The chapter to follow will survey the results obtained in related studies employing both similar and dissimilar psychomotor testing techniques, and will provide a broader foundation of knowledge for speculation as to the essential cause of psychomotor defect in the behavior disorders.

CHAPTER 8

SURVEY OF RELATED OBSERVATIONS

To give breadth to the picture of psychomotor function in mental disease, this chapter will take as its central theme reports by the many other workers who have studied psychomotor performance by individuals who exhibited one form or another of behavior deviation. This type of inquiry is certainly not new, for the value of including psychomotor observations in the attempt to understand mental illness was stressed by Kraepelin (73) and Bleuler (14) and other pioneers of systematic psychiatry. Since their day many investigators have performed experiments or made systematic observations on one phase or another of psychomotor activity which are of interest in the consideration of psychomotility in mental disease, and to this body of material are added the data of the present report.

The study of psychomotor function among normal individuals has demonstrated with clarity that what is often termed "psychomotor ability" is not in any sense a unitary factor, but is made up of a complex of heterogeneous specific abilities which show only slight tendencies to fall in clusters and no tendency at all to group systematically about a single central factor (116, 117, 118, 120, 121). This primary fact must be borne clearly in mind when discussing the interrelation of psychopathology and "psychomotor ability," for no single test of a single factor can represent psychomotor ability among the psychopathologic any more than it can among normal individuals. A more comprehensive view, then, must be formed from the pattern which emerges from a review of a number of studies of the problem which employ differing experimental approaches, each of which would individually possess only a limited generality. An integration of these may give some idea of the action of the broad range of human activities subsumed under the term *psychomotility* in the presence of behavior disorder.

Studies with the normal have made it clear that at least one general subdivision may justifiably be made among tests of psychomotor function, distinguishing *fine* from *gross* movement patterns (116, 117, 118). It will be recalled that the term *gross movement* has been used to refer to actions characterized by strength (labor, athletic, postural actions, etc.) and fine movement to refer to those coordinations in which the factor of strength is secondary to speed or precision, or both (hand and finger actions, e.g., typing, etc.). The focus of the present study has been on movements of the latter type, but to build a more rounded picture of psychomotility in mental disease, observations of both fine and gross psychomotor activities by subjects with behavior disorder will be included in the survey of related investigations.[1]

FINE PSYCHOMOTOR ACTIVITIES

Reaction time has unquestionably been the most extensively studied of the fine psychomotor responses of the mentally ill. Quantitative investigations of the nature of this response among psychotic subjects have been conducted since 1874 (98) on a wide variety of subjects for a wide variety of purposes. Several summaries of the results of these early applications of the reaction time method to the study of mental disease are available, and may be found in the reports of Wells and Kelley (137), Saunders and Isaacs (115), Huston, Shakow, and Riggs (52), Wulfeck (141) and Hunt and Cofer (48). Most of the early investigators reported finding a slowing of response among the psychotic subjects examined, although the groups under observation were small, the pathologic conditions of the patients highly varied, and the methods of measurement em-

[1] It was not thought to be particularly necessary to add to this report an extensive account of the material related to the specific techniques employed herein from outside the range of behavior disorder, although an understanding of the nature of these functions in subjects uncomplicated by mental disease is of primary importance in interpreting the data of pathologic cases. All of the methods employed are well-known psychologic measurement techniques, and related material may be found in the literature for each: (*reaction time,* 39, 93, 135, 140; *tapping,* 93, 109, 135; *dexterity,* 93, 133).

ployed often quite different. The largest and most carefully studied group reported to date is that of Huston, Shakow, and Riggs (52), who included measures of both simple and disjunctive reaction time in their broad investigation of motor function in schizophrenia. These experiments confirmed the general finding of both slowed times of minimal response and expanded variability of response which had been earlier indicated for psychotic subjects, and also presented data on the interrelation between the mean times of response and the severity of the psychosis as determined by a rating method. Positive correlations were found to exist indicating "better" performance (faster, less variable) by the more "cooperative" patients. In search of the reason for the prolonged reaction times they observed in psychosis, the same investigators and Rodnick and Shakow (112) have examined the effect of the preparatory interval —that is, the time between the "ready" signal and the onset of the stimulus—on reaction time, and report that the schizophrenic patient was less able to maintain a state of "readiness" to respond than was the comparable normal. The meaning of this as an explanation of the delays found in reaction time among schizophrenic subjects is not altogether clear, however, since Wulfeck (141) reports that the performance of schizophrenics is also slower on the reaction-coordination task, in which the subject does not depend upon external signals for initiating his response, but begins when he is ready and executes a simple response as quickly as possible. Most reports agree, however, that slowed response in the reaction time situation does occur in the various behavior disorders examined, and the data of the present experiment further extend our knowledge of reaction time in schizophrenia, its borderline conditions and psychoneurosis, and the interrelation of the measure with other types of psychomotor response and factors in the clinical status of the behavior disorder. The long history of investigation with the method and the ever increasing adequacy of measurement techniques make it appear that the finding of slowed reaction times, accompanied by an expansion in the variability of the measure for both individuals and groups, is a readily reproducible phenomenon in psychotic patients generally and schizophrenic patients in particular.

Studies of tapping speed in psychosis have also had a long

history of experimentation, but a much less active one than reaction time. This type of psychomotor measure has been applied, from time to time, since Kraepelin's day (72), to small groups of patients with a behavior disorder. The most extensive application of the method to a large group of psychotics was reported by Shakow and Huston (123) as part of their program to describe a large population of typical mental hospital patients in terms of motor functions at various levels of organization. Schizophrenic patients were found to be decidedly slower in their average tapping rates and more variable in their responses than were normal control subjects. A small group of manic-depressive patients, too limited to permit broad generalization, was also found to have slower tapping rates than normal individuals. King and Clausen (68, 69) have reported observing slowed tapping rates with both schizophrenic and pseudoneurotic schizophrenic patients; and Waldfogel, Finesinger, and Verzeano (136) found differences between a psychoneurotic group and a group of normal controls on tapping speed, although other inequalities in their groups caused them to question the genuine nature of this difference. Recently, Malmo and Andrews (86), while testing a new recording device for the measurement of foot-tapping with polyneuropathic subjects, reported an indication of hysterical tendencies to be associated with an irregular pattern of foot-tapping.

Probably closely related to these results on tests of maximal tapping speed is the matter of "personal tempo" measurement. Several investigators have reported on one variant or another of this type of psychomotor performance. In general, when subjects are asked to tap with the finger or hand at a rate "comfortable" to them, a characteristic rate is established for any given individual (called the "personal tempo") which has been found to be highly reliable (43, 111, 131); that is to say, values of the same order are obtained from one time of testing to another. Using this type of measurement method with both emotionally stable and emotionally unstable children, Chorus (20, 21, 22) has reported finding greater trial-to-trial and day-to-day variability of performance among emotionally unstable subjects. He relates this to the developmental finding that younger children are characteristically more variable than older ones on such performance, and interprets the increased variability of the unstable children, as compared with that of the stable group of the same age, as a sign of an immature personality. Meyerson and Landau (92) have reported that a mixed group of patients with various psychiatric disorders chose much lower "comfortable" rates of tapping speed than did a comparable group of matched control subjects. Probably related to these results are the findings of Wulfeck (141), who requested schizophrenic, manic-depressive, psychoneurotic and normal subjects to follow rhythmic patterns, both regular and irregular, set by the examiner after hearing the sequences through once. He reports that schizophrenics show a marked tendency to delay before beginning to follow the pattern signals, a lower mean number of taps and a greater length of tap-pressure than do normal individuals. The manic-depressive group also gave deviant responses, with the clinically observed heightened activity level of the manic patients and the retarded activity level of the depressed being reflected in the test results. Strong stereotypy in the tempo movements of schizophrenic patients has been reported by Tatarenko (131). Several investigators have also attempted to extend the meaning of the personal tempo type of measurement into the measurement of personality types among normal subjects, believing that records of rhythmic movements and changes from the naturally preferred rates may reveal character traits and reflections of the personality. The work of Nancken (97), Brunner (17), and Chorus (20, 21, 22) exemplifies this trend. The results of these studies on tapping speed and the personal tempo among subjects with a behavior disorder and those of the present report on speed of tapping by neurotic, pseudoneurotic schizophrenic, and chronic schizophrenic subjects would make it appear that an altered rate of tapping speed is a characteristic phenomenon to be found among patients suffering from a behavior disorder, one which manifests itself particularly in the performance of schizophrenics.

In attempting to integrate the results obtained by different investigators who have administered precision-dexterity tests of one sort or another to subjects suffering from a behavior disorder, one special consideration must be taken into account. The experiments on reaction time and tapping speed reported thus far, although performed with different types of apparatus and under many different experimental circumstances, have for the most part employed the same type of response movement from the subject in each instance: response with the preferred hand, and with a similar involvement of musculature and pattern of movement. We know from studies of the normal that the sense organ by which controlling information is received is of moderate importance in determining the characteristics of a psychomotor response, that the particular musculature employed—e.g., right or left arm, or leg—is of only slight importance, and that the pattern of movement involved is likely to be the most important consideration governing response (118). This statement may appear to go against the superficial evidence, but careful study reveals the fact that responses involving different movement patterns—reaction time and tapping speed, or tapping speed in vertical and horizontal planes, etc.—are usually low in their intercorrelation despite their superficial similarity. In view of this fact, there is probably less communality of function tested by different dexterity or precision tests than surface inspection would indicate, for they differ somewhat in the movement pattern required, and the sharpness of focus of test methods for this factor is probably less adequate than that of the tests of initiating and continuing movement. Several test methods seem to center about the qualities of movement called dexterity, precision, or steadiness, which reflect the degree of control exerted by the individual over the "nicety" of his movements. It is likely that both voluntary and involuntary factors are involved, precision being closer to the former and stationary steadiness to the latter.

Using simple dexterity tests of the ability to place, handle, and assemble small metal pieces, King and Clausen (68, 69) have reported reduced performance by schizophrenic and pseudoneurotic schizophrenic patients working at such tasks, and have found in their experimental groups that the degree of retardation observed in dextrous performance roughly paralleled clinical observations on the degree of disturbance present in behavior. King (62) has also reported a parallel between the degree of retardation in finger dexterity and the severity of behavior disturbance resulting from orbitofrontal psychosurgical operations. Huston and Shakow (50) have compared the eye-hand coordination of normal and schizophrenic subjects on stylus steadiness tasks, which measure the ability of a subject to hold a stylus suspended in a hole without touching the sides of the hole, for a graded series ranging from large to very small apertures. They found a poorer quality of performance by schizophrenes, accompanied by a greater variability of performance, with better performance being positively related to good cooperation. Waldfogel, Finesinger, and Verzeano (136) found the performance of psychoneurotic patients to be inferior to that of normal controls on a similar stylus task of eye-hand coordination, and reported a greater impairment of performance in the psychoneurotic group than for a normal control group under conditions of oxygen deprivation. Tasks of eye-hand coordination in tracking behavior on the prod meter and pursuit meter, which require the subject to maintain contact between a hand stylus and a moving target object, have been shown to reveal poorer performance by schizophrenic when compared with normal subjects, the degree of defect roughly paralleling the clinical estimate of behavior disturbance (49, 122). Retarded performance on a task of guiding behavior (eye-hand coordination in guiding a ball uphill past obstacles with a stylus of irregular shape) has also been demonstrated for psychoneurotics prior to oxygen deprivation experiments, with a greater relative decrement occurring than for normal subjects during the period of oxygen lack (91). The results of these experiments with their various approaches to the factor of precision-dexterity among the mentally ill and those cited in the body of this report on normal, psychoneurotic, pseudoneurotic schizophrenic, and chronic schizophrenic subjects would make it appear that some loss of precision-dexterity ability is present in behavior disorder and that this retardation is greater in patients with more marked clinical behavior deviations.

These reports summarize the work most directly bearing on the techniques used in the present study and dealing with the time characteristics of initiating, continuing, and exercising control over simple, fine psychomotor movements. The results are in obvious agreement with those obtained in the present experiment, and indicate that the disturbance of fine psychomotor ability in behavior disorder is of sufficient magnitude and generality to be reflected by any of a number of different testing techniques. There is also a considerable fund of experimental information which may be added to this, including observations on fine motor movements of a greater complexity and with varying degrees of interaction with other psychologic capacities. Performance on the tasks described up to this point may be assumed to be relatively free of connection with other characteristics of the individual, such as intelligence, occupation, culture, socio-economic status, education, language ability, etc. (93, 118, 135, 140). As we move higher up the integrative scale, however, to performance on more complex tasks, such factors come into increasing prominence in performance and assume a far greater role in influencing the final responses obtained. It is manifestly impossible to report all of the details on subject groups which would be necessary to make a full evaluation of the entry of such considerations into psychomotor performance, even if these were completely known, which often they are not. It must be borne in mind, therefore, that in addition to the rather independent nature of most psychomotor performance, the degree to which each relates to other psychologic and cultural characteristics of the individuals studied must be taken into account in any final evaluation of psychomotor performance at the higher integrative levels. Even the terms used are indicative of the basic situation, for by higher levels and grades of integration we usually mean that more than one system is involved (e.g., speech and motor) and that various levels of difficulty (intelligence-learning factors) are concerned.

Wulfeck (141) has recently reported a broad research into psychomotor performance by the mentally disordered on tasks which he has termed those of *intermediate integrative level;* he states, "by intermediate levels of integration is meant those movements dependent upon the execution of a series of simple, non-identical, sequential coordinations or elements of movements linked together in patterns of movements involving both the preparation to respond and sustained activity of short duration." The application of tests of psychomotor movement of this type to situations of behavior disorder form a logical extension from the observations earlier reported and of the type employed in the present experiment into the sphere of adaptive and integrated action. Wulfeck has reported on performance by normal subjects, psychoneurotics, manic-depressives, and schizophrenics on seven different psychomotor tests and has compared the performance of each of these groups with all others. The tests used were: the estimation of known sizes, the pneumoergograph, star tracings, reaction coordination, and the following of rhythmic patterns. Retardation was found to characterize performance by the schizophrenic group on all tests, and the same was true to a lesser but still quite detectable extent for the manic-depressives, while performance by the psychoneurotic group approximated that of the normal subjects. From the comparative data obtained, Wulfeck concluded that schizophrenia is a disease which reduces the ability of the patient to perform adaptive motor acts at the intermediate levels of integration, but that psychoneurosis seemed to have little influence on the ability to perform adaptive acts at this level of coordination.

The use of other psychomotor tests involving an integrated response have shown much the same type of retardation by subjects with a behavior disorder. Peters (103) has applied the mirror tracing test as a measure of social maladaptation by observing its performance by normal subjects, adolescent delinquents, prisoners, and psychotics, the last three groups including individuals in difficulty with society in one way or another. The task set is a simple one, tracing a star pattern under visual guidance by means of a mirror that reverses the habitual eye-hand relation, thus requiring a novel adjustment on the part of the subject in the form of all movements made. Peters found that the time required for the execution of this task and the percentage failing of completion consistently showed larger mean scores for the socially non-adapted groups than for the control subjects tested. The fact that these are independent measures was felt to make the results doubly significant. A poor level of performance on a similar mirror-tracing task has also been reported by Garrison (40) as characterizing the preoperative status of psychotic patients who were to undergo frontal topectomy operations, and this same population also exhibited markedly inferior performance on a continuous-performance task of spatial problem solving (63). The Bender Gestalt test, which requires the subject to draw pencilled copies of a series of geometric forms, has had widespread clinical use in recent years, especially as an aid in the possible detection of organic brain damage. Although the emphasis in the interpretation of performance on this test has remained, for the most part, on the *Gestalten* aspects of design reproduction, the figures drawn are nonetheless psychomotor productions and the parallels found between organic brain damage and behavior disorder and faulty design reproduction are of related interest to our main theme. More complete discussions of this approach and its clinical and experimental findings have been recently reported elsewhere (9, 12, 101) and will not be repeated here, other than to point out the fact that this test method has been found to be of value in the diagnosis of organic and behavior disorder. The study of Townsend (134) on copying ability in children reinforces the notion that performance on the Bender type of task contains strong elements of spatial-form organization rather than a connection with simple timed psychomotor performance, and emphasizes the presence of spatial elements in the test and their interaction with movement patterns. A similar situation probably prevails in the faulty performance by individuals with behavior disorder on tests of block design, manikin-assembly, marble-patterns, and kindred tasks reported by a large number of different investigators (80, 108, 130, 138).

The fund of clinical and experimental evidence from studies of the performance of behavior deviates on the Porteus Maze test also yields evidence of a disruption in psychomotor performance by subjects with a behavior disorder. Porteus (105) and others (63, 78, 107) have discussed more fully elsewhere the essential behavior traits measured by this test, which requires a subject to trace his way through a series of paper-and-pencil mazes of graded difficulty. In brief, the test is designed to measure intelligence, with specific emphasis on social intelligence and self-sufficiency, and laying full stress on the importance of such factors as planfulness, zeal, and vigilance in determining an individual's social sufficiency. The ability to act in a "socially intelligent," planful, or zealous manner is notably impaired clinically in the presence of behavior disorder, and such imperfections are magnified still further by the exacerbation of psychotic symptoms usually associated with the immediate postoperative period following frontal lobe psychosurgery (44). It would be expected, and it has been shown, that performance on the maze test would be affected by both of these conditions. The level of performance achieved by subjects suffering from chronic behavior disorder has been found by Porteus (105) and others (63, 107) to be below the level established by comparable normal control subjects, and increases in the degree of psychotic impairment have been demonstrated to occur immediately following psychosurgery (63, 107, 124, 125). It would appear that the functions sampled by this technique are limited in behavior disorder, and further research is needed to determine to what extent this may be traced to spatial-form factors in the psychomotor performance and to what extent it may be attributed to such factors as psychomotor initiative and organization, and to furnish further information on the nature of the relationship between maze performance and behavior traits.

A number of writers have suggested the possibility of using tasks of psychomotor integration of one sort or another as measures of personality traits and functioning within the range of normal behavior (3, 4, 8, 13, 19, 30, 32, 35, 42, 53, 94, 127). These investigators have usually reported finding parallels between the adequacy of patterns of psychomotor performance on such tasks as tracking, rhythmic movement, ergography, letter-printing, figure drawing, model reproduction while blindfolded, etc., and various character traits of the individual subjects performing these tasks. To date, such studies have suffered from an absence of adequate validating criteria, but the trend toward a positive relationship between inadequate psychomotor performance and personality deviation is relatively clear.

As the psychopathologic states of behavior are usually clinically characterized by disorganized emotional responses of one sort or another, information gathered from studies of the interrelation of psychomotor performance and disturbed emotion in the normal individual may be of some help in trying to understand the processes and mechanisms involved in behavior disorder. A number of experimental inquiries have been made into the possible interrelation of psychomotor performance and states of disturbed emotion in the normal individual by means of the "association-motor" technique. This method requires the performance of a simple psychomotor task while verbal associations to emotionally linked material are explored. The psychomotor performance record is then analyzed for signs indicative of areas of emotional conflict in terms of clear departures from the ordinary in the manner of psychomotor response. Luria (83) placed great emphasis on the disorganization of behavior under emotional stress and emphasized the need to study these phenomena centrally. He postulated that the dynamic influence of emotion caused by conflict spread to motor habits, and that by the observation of these habits we might find clues to the action of the central processes. Believing the speech centers and the control of the preferred hand to be closely related neurally, he instructed subjects to respond verbally to questions and stimulus words and to make simultaneously a voluntary pressure (on a rubber bulb) with the preferred hand. The voluntary motor response was recorded together with a continuous record of tremor in the non-preferred hand (involuntary response).

Insofar as states of behavior disorder are marked by emotional disorder, the results of Luria's experiments and the many that followed using his technique are relevant to our theme. Experiments on natural affects (83), the detection of guilt or deception (10, 11, 18, 37, 75, 83, 114) and the effects of hypnotically induced complexes (51, 83) have furnished considerable evidence of the phenomenon of disorganized motor behavior in the presence of real and artificial affects. This takes the form of premature or prolonged voluntary pressures, or multiple responses or failures to respond altogether for movements by the preferred hand, and increased tremor of the non-preferred hand in the presence of conflict or strong emotion. The technique has also been applied to the study of psychoneurosis by Barnacle, Ebaugh and Lemere (7) who compared the responses of neurotic and normal subjects and reported finding characteristic differences in the reaction patterns of anxiety neurotics, hysterics, obsessive-compulsives, and normal persons. These authors say that the association-motor method has proved more effective than measures of blood pressure, respiration, galvanic skin response, or word-association alone, and that "association-motor studies have a definite place in the investigation and treatment of the psychoneuroses." Pressing nearer the borderline, Albino (1) has reported his attempts to distinguish neuroticism among groups of normal subjects by means of the association-motor method, and has reported that some of the scores succeed in making such a distinction while others do not. Little is known about association-motor performance by psychotic subjects. Malmo et al.

(90) have employed a modification of the technique to evaluate the reactions of psychotic patients to stress and this will be reported later in that context. Berrien (10, 11), using interruptions in rhythmic finger oscillations by subjects while under questioning about details of their clinical histories, does report the use of a related technique with psychotic subjects, finding deviant psychomotor response to some of the crucial questions asked in the interview.

In addition to the observations available on fine psychomotor functioning in the presence of behavior disorder, data from research conducted on the influence of special experimental conditions on the mentally ill may be cited as an indication of the effects of change in the status of such patients upon their fine psychomotor performance. The work of Malmo and his associates on stressful conditions is significant in this regard. This group of investigators has applied experimental stress to groups of subjects suffering from mental disorder and observed its effects upon psychomotor functioning by means of a modified Luria technique. When a painful stimulus in the form of radiant heat applied to the skin was used as an experimental stress, with the blood lymphocyte count as an indicator of the presence of stress, Malmo et al. (89) found that psychoneurotic subjects reacted in a quite different fashion from normal control subjects in that their degree of control over psychomotor behavior was inferior. When a further experiment was arranged so that the subjects could signal (by pressing a button) when the stimulus was beginning to be painful, but were under instruction not to withdraw from the apparatus, psychoneurotic and early schizophrenic subjects showed less control over withdrawal movements in the situation than did normals, and the investigators concluded that they exhibited "an impairment of motor control and a reduction of the capacity to inhibit reactions in the interests of superior adjustment." Extending their work to observations on the effects of psychologic stress, Malmo et al. (90) required psychoneurotics, acute psychotics, chronic schizophrenics, and normal controls to make difficult, speeded perceptual discriminations while Luria type recordings of activity with the hands were made simultaneously. In every case greater psychomotor disturbance and irregularity were found among the patients than among the normal controls, although their scores on perceptual performance were practically identical. Malmo, Shagass, and Davis (88) have also reported an experiment in which electromyographic responses of the right forearm to strong auditory stimulation were compared for normal and psychoneurotic subjects. They found similar initial (startle-type) reactions in both groups, but the psychoneurotic group was characterized by a much greater "after-discharge" than the normal, continuing to gain in response after the normal had begun to return to the base level. These results were interpreted as indicative of a defective regulatory system with a partial failure of cortical inhibition of after-discharge in the skeletal muscular system. McFarland and Barach (91) have studied the responses of psychoneurotics to variations in oxygen tension, as compared with a normal control group, and found that the stress of oxygen deprivation produced relatively greater impairments in performance by psychoneurotic subjects on tasks of choice reaction, mirror tracing and eye-hand coordination. In similar experiments, but with lesser changes in the degree of oxygen deprivation, Waldfogel, Finesinger, and Verzeano (136) failed to record significantly greater relative changes in the performance of a psychoneurotic group on tests of simple reaction time, disjunctive reaction time, tapping speed, and stylus steadiness, although a trend in this direction was noted.

We will not attempt to trace here the effects of stress of various sorts on normal psychomotor performance, although it has been pointed out that the consequent minor disorganization forms a midpoint between normal, uncomplicated function and the conditions of mild chronic disorder such as the neuroses (80). Material relating to the effects upon psychomotor performance by normal individuals of experimentally produced stresses (e.g., pain or fear) and the systematic observation of psychomotor performance by normal subjects exposed to naturally stressful conditions (e.g., extreme states of sleep loss or starvation) may be found elsewhere in the literature (34, 80, 132, 135).

Therapeutic alterations and changes in the clinical status of patients with behavior disorders furnish another situation in which concomitant effects on psychomotor performance may be noted. Brower and Oppenheim (16) have compared the before-and-after electroconvulsive therapy performance records of a group of patients diagnosed as involutional, manic-depressive, and depressive with some schizophrenic features, including in their test battery such psychomotor tasks as figure drawing, hand dynamometer, tapping speed, and mirror tracing. In general, a clinical improvement in this patient group resulted from the therapy applied, and this improvement was reflected in an increased adequacy of performance on all psychomotor tests of the battery. Peters and Jones (104) have recently emphasized the value of using psychomotor measurement methods in tracing the course of clinical alterations as compared with other types of psychologic evaluation. These workers applied to a series of schizophrenic patients receiving group psychotherapy a battery of tests including, along with projective and other evaluations, the mirror tracing test, the Porteus Maze test and the draw-a-person test. They found the psychomotor tests to be definitely sensitive to changes in the status of the group in therapy, particularly when compared with the relative insensitivity of other evaluative procedures. The experiments of King et al. (70) have also shown that when the tests described in the body of the present report are employed for making periodic measurements on individual schizophrenic patients receiving therapeutic electrical stimulation of the septal region of the midbrain, the adequacy of performance on the psychomotor battery parallels quite clearly the clinical course of patients who respond, or fail to respond, to the therapy. King (62) and King and Clausen (68, 69) have also demonstrated that the period of symptomatic exacerbation of psychosis which characteristically follows frontal lobe surgery for the relief of mental disease is associated with a decline in psychomotor performance on tests of fine psychomotor ability; and the same has been shown to hold true for performance on the Porteus Maze test by several investigators (63, 106, 107, 124, 125). Our information is much too incomplete at present to attempt to appraise the relative merits of different types of psychomotor measurement as an index of changing clinical status, and that is not our purpose here. It is worth noting, however, that the reports of research conducted to date indicate that the convenient measures of fine psychomotor performance show a definite parallel to the course of the clinical manifestations of behavior disorder.

The results of the many investigations of one or another aspect of the interrelation of fine psychomotor performance and behavior disorder cited above attempt to show, by grouping these varied studies together, the directness of the association between fine psychomotor performance and abnormalities of behavior. The division of psychomotor activities into fine and gross movements which has been followed is, however, only a matter of convenience, based upon the divisions made when such activities are studied in the normal. There is every reason to extend the survey of the research available on to the interrelation of gross psychomotor movements and behavior disorder. Perhaps midway between the consideration of fine and gross movements lie certain of the "work" measures. These, although often involving only one limb and therefore more closely resembling fine movement patterns, require a degree of energy output that also gives them a similarity to the gross bodily movements. Since they are to this extent "transitional," they will fall in this order in the discussion of related work.

Kraepelin (74) made use of psychomotor work tasks which extended over periods of time to bring out more clearly inadequacies in the performance of the mentally ill. It was learned that, in the presence of behavior disorder, performance on many different types of work tasks was characterized by large decrements in performance beyond those normally expected; this was especially true of the records of schizophrenics. Wulfeck (142) has more recently observed performance on an ergograph by normal subjects, psychoneurotics, manic-depressives, and schizophrenics. He reports lessened performance for psychotics when compared with normal subjects, scoring the number of pressures/time, but found no reliable differences between performance by psychoneurotic and by normal subjects. The scores obtained by schizophrenics were particularly low. Mailloux and Newburger (84) have also reported a pronounced lowering of the work rate among psychotics, and have examined the work records of their mentally ill subjects for "blocks"—defined as a period of inactivity which exceeded the average response time (of a "unit" of the work) by a factor of 3. Such blocks occur in sustained, homogeneous work performance by normal individuals and are reported for the control group of this series; the number of such blocks was, however, found to be much more frequent among the psychotics examined. King (63) has also reported a low rate of continuous problem solving (spatial problems) among schizophrenic patients. More research is needed on this phase of the problem, but from the evidence available it would appear that more limited work rates, unusual work decrements, and more frequent work blockages occur in homogeneous psychomotor work in the presence of behavior disorder than among comparable normal control subjects.

GROSS PSYCHOMOTOR ACTIVITIES

Turning now to observations on gross motor behavior, it must be stated at the outset that some of the observations recorded are not separate from a condition of behavior disorder, but are part of the pattern of gross disorder on which a diagnosis of behavior disorder itself is made. The presence of a certain number of motor aberrations in mental disease has long been noted, and although these symptoms are far from invariable, they form in part the material on which diagnosis of the several categories of mental disorder is based. No attempt will be made to elaborate on the clinical observation of such motor patterns here, as they have been treated in the psychiatric literature since the beginning days of systematic psychiatry (14, 73). We will instead attempt to focus on less common methods of observation and on data obtained by measurement techniques specifically designed to throw the motor elements into relief in comparisons between mental patients and normal persons, groups of patients, and patients under varying circumstances.

An example of this approach has been the recent adaptation of time-sampling techniques from the animal laboratory to the study of behavior disorder and factors in the bodily expression of mental states (54, 55, 60, 61). This method has proved its value in helping to understand the underlying mechanisms of the behavior patterns of animals, and has been applied to groups of psychotic patients with a similar purpose and point of view. In essence, it involves the recording of systematic observations on the overt motor behavior of subjects, without their notice, when they are placed in a standardized situation designed to elicit some response; e.g., with animals, nest building behavior, etc., and with human beings, social interchange with other persons, etc. Jones (54) has reported making such observations for descriptive purposes on a large group of psychotic patients, using many separated short periods of observation, and Kinder (60, 61) has applied a similar technique for the evaluation of possible changes in gross motor behavior following frontal topectomy for the relief of mental disease. Neither of these investigators was specifically concerned with making comparisons of the activity of their psychotic groups with that of normal subjects, and detailed data relevant to this fundamental point must await further study. It is clear from their reports, however, that the method makes possible the quantitative notation of the characteristics of gross motor behavior among the mentally ill, and that it reflects those distinctions between the bodily movements of normal and abnormal persons which are apparent to ordinary clinical observation and should thus greatly extend the depth and subtlety of such observations. Jones has also reported on the use of time-sampling technique as a way of evaluating the effects of minor stress situations on the "nervous movements" of normal subjects (personal movements such as scratching, facial contractions, general body fidgeting, etc.). Observing children in control and experimental situations, with mental arithmetic and inhibition of micturition serving as minor stress situations, Jones reports (55, 56) an increase in "nervous movements" by the subjects in each of these situations beyond that shown by their earlier behavior and by control subjects.

Page (100) has studied the day and night motility patterns followed by normal and psychotic individuals, recording them by means of kymographic tracings of movement made while the subjects were lying in a hospital bed. He reports that such records made on small groups of normal persons, catatonic schizophrenics, manic-depressives and Parkinsonian patients reflect the common clinical observation of little daytime activity in the catatonic patients, and a high level of activity among the manic patients, with the normal individuals and Parkinsonian patients falling in between these groups. The night-time records for all groups were found to resemble one another much more closely.

Several studies which employ the rating scale method of notation of ward activity or activity observed during psychiatric interviews or psychologic testing have confirmed the clinical observation of differential styles of psychomotor activity among mental patients of different diagnostic categories (25, 70, 82, 85, 113). These scales, by their quantitative nature, have also proved their effectiveness as reflectors of the clinical status of patients undergoing therapy of various sorts, for a "normalizing" of gross psychomotor disturbances is one of the regular accompaniments of improvement in condition (70, 85, 96). These various notational methods are relatively recent attempts to render quantitative observations made on gross psychomotor movement of the sort which have long been used qualitatively in forming clinical and diagnostic impressions. They have the added advantage, however, of being more objective and more searching in their scrutiny than ordinary subjective impressions based on limited observation. Although up to the present their use has extended little beyond the verification of the fact that certain characteristic styles of motility do exist among the mentally ill and the tracing of the hospital course of mental patients in response to therapies, they obviously present us with a powerful method for the more detailed investigation of psychomotor elements in the behavior disorders.

It would be particularly interesting to be able to review data drawn from the systematic observation of gross psychomotor patterns of the mentally ill at various developmental levels as the individual passes through the growth and maturational process. This is, of course, largely impossible, since the behavior disorders do not usually clearly manifest themselves until after adult status has been achieved. The reconstructional method of the case history, although attempting to describe early psychomotor patterns as well as possible (e.g., noting such things as "awkward child," "bizarre postures," etc.), actually gives little or no systematic evidence of the course of psychomotor development among individuals later afflicted with mental disease. The gross defects present in the developmental growth of motor abilities among the mentally deficient are, of course, a well known and limited exception, and are considered to be a part of the generally retarded nature of these conditions (5, 15, 41, 45, 76, 138). Perhaps the most pertinent of the available observations of the interrelation of emotional disorder and developmental psychomotor defects come from the study of individuals with the speech defects of stuttering and stammering. Many investigations (5, 31, 71, 102, 129, 139) have shown the presence of faulty psychomotor performance in the presence of these speech disorders. There appears to be a psychomotor defect present as well as the difficulty in speech in children studied at various age levels, which has been shown in comparisons with normal children on gymnastic tests, motor "fitness" tests (e.g., the Oseretzky Scale), balancing, amplitude of joint movement, respiration, and so on.

Several methods have been applied to normal individuals and those with pathology of behavior which single out a part of the activity of the total organism for observation, such as measures of psychomotor tension while performing other tasks, electromyograms of tension in the skeletal musculature, records of respiration, etc. These activities, while not so clearly psychomotor in nature or immediately purposeful in the context of the moment as most we have discussed, do come under cortical control and may be said to reflect psychomotor activity of the total organism to at least a partial extent. Wulfeck (142) has reported making measures of voluntary muscle tension simultaneously with performance on other psychomotor tasks among normal individuals and schizophrenic, manic-depressive, and psychoneurotic patients. He reports that the habitual base-line tension, measured in the non-preferred hand prior to performance with the preferred hand, was highest among manic patients and next highest among schizophrenics, with depressives, normal subjects, and psychoneurotics following in that order. When he compared the total changes in tension while simultaneously performing motor tasks with the preferred hand, schizophrenics showed the greatest changes and normal subjects the least, with the manic and depressive groups both showing greater tensional changes than the normal and psychoneurotic groups, which were nearly the same. In experiments in which electromyographic recordings of muscular tensions were made on normal individuals and those with histories of pathologic behavior, Malmo and Shagass (87) found a greater number of neck muscle potentials in groups of anxiety neurotics, early schizophrenics and a mixed patient group (depressives, psychopaths, etc.) than for normal control subjects. Malmo, Shagass, and Davis (88) have also reported finding higher mean amplitudes of electromyographic response of the right arm in a group of psychoneurotic subjects when compared with a group of normal control subjects. Respiration measurements made by Malmo and Shagass

(87) upon the groups of anxiety neurotics, early schizophrenics, mixed patients, and normal subjects have shown a greater percentage of deviations of rate and amplitude for the anxiety and early schizophrenic groups, while the mixed group did not differ from that of control subjects. In an extensive study of respiration movements in normal, neurotic, and psychotic subjects, Clausen (23) has reported faster breathing rates for neurotic and psychotic subjects than for comparable normal controls, and has also found differences between the groups on qualitative evaluations, such as the regularity within a given recording, expiration pauses, sharpness of the inspiration-expiration transition, etc.

Approaching the matter in a different way, some psychotherapists have recently placed stress on the value of making observations on psychomotor postures, attitudes, mannerisms, and expressions as an aid in grasping the psychodynamics of disordered behavior in individual cases. Ascher (6) has emphasized the fact that frequently the motor behavior of a patient will offer valuable clues regarding his emotional conflicts and serve as an indicator of personality functioning. He reviews the work of others relevant to this attitude, and suggests the inclusion and more extensive use of motor observations in the patient's history and chart as an index of improvement in the course of treatment. Mittelmann (95) has studied the psychodynamics of motility in infants, children, and adults, using psychoanalytic data supplemented by "drawing" methods and motion picture analysis. He suggests the presence of a skeletal motor drive, which is both an urge in its own right and which is connected with nearly all other motivational strivings, physiologic and emotional. The vast literature on expressive movement in normal and abnormal subjects is probably related to this general context (2, 140).

This review of related experiments, although it makes no pretense to complete coverage of so complex a topic, should serve to indicate with clarity that disturbances in psychomotility are indeed to be found in behavior disorder. Imperfections in psychomotor performance are reflected in a wide variety of measures at many levels of complexity and organization for both fine and gross body movements, with remarkably few, if any, negative instances reported. However crude or incomplete our knowledge may be at the present time, there appears to be a sufficient and significant body of evidence that behavior disorder finds its parallel in impaired psychomotor function. This phenomenon, whatever its eventual explanation, represents a fact of clear importance to both theorist and practitioner concerned with the broad problem of mental disease. In practice, these findings might be put to immediate and fruitful use in recording and measuring a correlate of disordered behavior, of which we have so few that are reliable and objective in nature, as an aid in diagnosis or in maintaining a record of the status of patients in the course of treatment, or as a research tool in attempting to estimate the effects of new and untried therapies. Both theorist and clinician will want to know much more about why this parallel exists, and a great many more details of its extent, degree, and validity, problems which may be settled only by further research. Does the array of positive evidence of psychomotor imperfection at many levels of complexity imply the presence in behavior disorder of some single factor, psychologic or physical, which cuts across all types of psychomotor performance, resulting in the simultaneous impairment of disparate behavior measures, or is a thorough-going partial disorganization of psychomotor function a basic characteristic of mental disease? Further study and research may be depended upon to provide us with the eventual answer. We may, in the interim, be able to facilitate the solution of the problem, or at least aid in the attack upon it, by a consideration of the position as it is currently known. The chapter to follow will attempt to present a basic position and attitude toward psychomotility as a factor in animate, and particularly human, existence which may help to render understandable and more cohesive the assorted and empirically unrelated bits of information which we have already at hand.

CHAPTER 9

PSYCHOMOTILITY: NORMAL AND ABNORMAL

THE data recorded in this experiment offer a clear demonstration of defective fine psychomotor performance among patients suffering from a behavior disorder, and, further, describe a direct relationship of considerable subtlety between speed in fine psychomotor performance and the degree of disorder present in behavior. What may account for these findings? In seeking an answer to this question, the first step taken has been to explore the results of a number of related investigations to include as many facts as possible from which to attempt the formulation of an hypothesis about the interrelation of psychomotor performance and mental disease. The weight of the evidence from such a broad survey, extending to many types of psychomotor performance other than those reported in the present experiment, leads to the definite conclusion that retardation and faulty control are exhibited in the psychomotor performance of the mentally ill at many different levels of response organization. The occurrence of a defect in so many different phases of psychomotor activity, of which the data of the present experiment form but a part, thus appears to be the primary finding in need of an explanation. There is a need for an hypothesis which would relate the disturbances of psychomotility in behavior disorder to the psychopathologic disorder, which must of necessity be broad in its composition to include the many different influences which bear upon psychomotor response. What are the characteristics of psychomotor activity or the qualities of psychomotor response which might be thought to make this form of human activity particularly subject to disorder—more specifically to retardation and faulty control—

in mental disease? To attempt an answer to this question we must consider something of the nature of psychomotor responsiveness as a basic psychophysiologic capacity, and also something of what is known of the essential defect present in the behavior disorders.

We may begin by considering, in the most general terms, the role of movement and of motor responsiveness to stimulation in animate existence. The human observer, on introspection, is likely to attach relatively slight importance to movement phenomena *per se* as representing an integral part of his activities in adjusting to the world about him. There is a tendency to regard movement, or the actual response made in a given situation, as a more or less executive function; something which is put in train only after a mental decision upon a course of action has been made. The separation of thought from action is not, however, quite so simple or direct. We must first recall that the ability to think about, and mentally plan a response not yet made, is a decidedly human adult characteristic, and that a more direct connection between motor response and stimulation, internal or external, is a biologic characteristic present long before the development of a conscious mind, either in the species or in the individual. All animate forms achieve some degree of motor response to stimulation, from the most primitive life forms to man, and we need not consider this capacity for active response to be exclusively dependent upon the presence of a conscious mind capable of trial activity in the form of conscious thought. It is also apparent, on closer observation, that even in the behavior of the adult human being, response to stimulation by movement is not the simple executive function of an abstract mind, but that motor responsiveness is definitely interactive in the psychologic processes of attention, perception, and learning, aiding in the achievement of more efficient patterns of response. This may be clearly seen in simple trial-and-error learning, where the elements of the situation to be adjusted to are difficult to abstract, in the acquisition of all skills, in the presence of strong emotion, and so on. Experimental situations, as well as objective observations made in natural life contexts, provide many indications that changes in active behavior may occur prior to a conscious recognition of all of the elements governing response. Although introspective analysis may tend to regard the response process itself as more or less automatic and secondary to the fact of mentation, so distinct a separation of the processes is probably unjustified in man, where both conscious and non-conscious actions remain useful forms of life adjustment, and does not apply at all to the subhuman animal orders. The power of movement, then, appears to be a characteristic shown by all animals from simplest to most complex, which serves as a primary method by which they adapt themselves to the circumstances about them. The more elaborate and more highly evolved animal life forms exhibit a far greater subtlety of possible movement and response adaptiveness, but continue to show a direct linkage between the needs of the organism at the moment and the activities to which it is impelled. It seems most unlikely that the development of conscious thought in man has completely displaced this basic adaptational mechanism as an important element in the adjustment of the individual to his environment. Although its operation may be overshadowed and subject to a different type of control owing to the presence of conscious mind, the biologic linkage remains intact and the capacity for motor responsiveness continues to play a primary role in human adaptation. Sperry (128) has put the matter directly and in more positive terms. He conceives of the nervous system as a structure intended specifically for the function of transforming sensory patterns into patterns of motor coordination, and further believes the sole product of brain function to be that of motor coordination, all subjective phenomena being simple byproducts. He has said, "The entire output of our thinking machine consists of nothing but patterns of motor coordination . . . . Cerebration, essentially, serves to bring into motor behavior additional refinement, increased direction toward distant, future goals and greater over-all adaptiveness and survival value."

We may turn now to a consideration, also in the most general terms, of what appears to be the essential nature of the disorder in behavior present in mental disease. The actual etiology of most mental disease is, at present, still unknown. It is characterized, descriptively, by behavior which is considered to be odd or unusual to the extent that persons so afflicted are a danger or a nuisance to themselves or others. The general terms most often used to describe such behavior of the mentally ill are *maladjustment* and *maladaptation,* implying the presence of a reaction pattern which is not only unusual for the individual, differing from that of the normal person, but also faulty or defective, an inadequate adjustment to the total situation. These faulty adjustments are expressed in the details of behavior as symptoms, which are individual and particular errors indicative of a basically faulty over-all reaction pattern of adjustment. We might expect, or at least postulate, that an indication of such a basic fault might be found in so fundamental an adaptive mechanism as the capacity for motor responsiveness. If the mental diseases are properly described as conditions of faulty adaptation, we might expect to observe a central error in this disturbance by a study of psychomotor response.

Regarded in this sense, the defective psychomotor response of the mentally ill which has been recorded in this experiment, and those defects and indications of faulty control noted in other, related investigations, may be thought to serve as an indication of a faulty condition of adaptation to the environment; i.e., the registration of inefficiencies in a basic adaptational mechanism. To be sure, the data presented here and what is known at present from the work of others do not serve as proof of such a general hypothesis. The findings are suggestive, however, and further experimentation based on this point of view may more nearly test the value of such an assumption. If the existence of the postulated relationship proves in time to be substantial, it also holds promise as an aid to our understanding of the nature of mental illness itself, for it would relate, in part, the psychopathologic disorders to the operation of a normal, basic life process.

Lest it be thought that the simple arm and finger movements described here, or other similar forms of psychomotor response, are too simple and everyday affairs to reflect basic disturbances of the total organism, it should be recalled that just such measures are found to be effective, where measures of more complex behavior are not, in reflecting psychologic alteration: when drugs of various sorts are present in the body, when alcohol is in the bloodstream, in fatigue states, with loss of sleep, oxygen deprivation and other forms of stress. They may be seen to vary with cycles of the body temperature, and so on. They exhibit maturation in childhood and decline in senescence; they are reduced, when not eliminated, by structural damage to the central nervous system, and largely disappear in sleep and under anesthesia. Their very simplicity appears to add to their value as indicators of the body working under handicap, in that their few connections with the higher psychologic or physical systems result in fewer compensation effects. That is to say, when a limiting condition is present, the organism cannot mobilize to compensate by an increased effort for inefficient action at this basic level as it can at higher levels; e.g., an extreme lack of sleep will have more effect on simple psychomotor activities than on the ability to do mental arithmetic or to operate a complex rangefinder (135).

The further study of psychomotility and of motor responsiveness in both humans and the lower animals seems indicated in several respects. Fundamentally, we need to know much more of the interrelation of psychomotility to other psychologic characteristics of the individual, such as emotion, intelligence, temperament, etc. Although our literature on motor and psychomotor behavior is already enormous (33, 93, 135, 140), we appear to be at only the beginning stage of understanding how the capacity for motor responsiveness is related to other characteristics of the organism. Much of what we have, at present, is drawn from very limited contexts, such as that gathered by the application of specific tests as an aid in the selection of workers who must exercise manual skills of many different sorts, e.g., sewing machine operators, small parts packers, etc. The practical finding that selection tests must be specific for each particular job is, in part, a reflection of the high degree of independence demonstrated in the many actions of which the human adult is capable. There is a need for broader study and for formulating and testing hypotheses more closely related to the total adaptiveness of the organism. It has been suggested that the development of more complex nervous structures accompanies the evolution of more efficient control of motor responsiveness and a more adequate adaptation to the environment, leading, ultimately to the development of mind in man. We can scarcely overemphasize the importance of this basic substrate in gaining an understanding of the development of the higher human psychologic characteristics.

There is a need also for broadening the study of the neural structures involved, for in this respect, as well as psychologically, the response capacities are not well understood. In our attempts to relate the working of brain structure to the workings of mind, the pattern of anatomic development of the nervous system has tended to stress the importance of afferent above that of efferent development. The location of the sense organs in the periphery has made it possible to observe their mode of action and steady elaboration as one ascends the phyletic scale. Particularly for the so-called distance receptors, the high degree of specificity in end-organ action has made it possible also to make observations on the projection of these nerve systems in the brain (36). There is less directness observable in the corresponding development of response characteristics, however, for the equivalent of the "end-organs" concerned are centrally located in the brain, less accessible to observation, and not easily defined or understood as systematic structures. The way in which they originate patterns of appropriate neural impulse for a motor response is also much more difficult to comprehend than the structural arrangements which permit the sensory end-organs to translate physical data from the environment into sensory neural impulse.[1] Throughout the present report, the terms *psychomotor* and *motor responsiveness* have been used to emphasize our concern with end-result actions as a unit of response, not simply the peripheral neural or muscular components. It is in this broader sense that further neurologic studies are most needed. There is also a continuing need for further exploration of the psychomotor response characteristics for all conditions of adaptational disorder: those resulting from known or suspected causes, such as senility, feeblemindedness, or several of the physical diseases, e.g., hypertension; and those with unknown causes, such as other mental diseases than those reported here, e.g., the toxic psychoses.

Whether or not further experimentation will tend to substantiate the speculative explanation offered above of the nature of the disorder in psychomotor response found in mental disease, the retardation phenomena observed in this experiment and in the reports of related investigations remain facts in themselves which

[1] It would be tempting to pursue neurologic speculation further, for the relevance of the neural element is of undoubted importance in understanding psychomotor adaptive behavior. This would be a closely allied, yet different approach to the subject matter. The neurologic method of further study of the role of movement in animate existence is also being pursued in this laboratory and will be made the subject of a separate report.

suggest a practical method of assisting in the difficult problem of the diagnosis of mental disorder, and, more importantly, provide a possible method for the measurement of the status of a behavior disorder at any given moment. An example of such usage is the recent application of the same psychomotor test battery described in this report as a research method of registering changes in the clinical status of patients receiving electrophysiologic stimulation of the septal region of the brain (70). In this study it was found that the measures of psychomotor performance paralleled directly the changes seen in the clinical estimates of the degree of disorder in behavior, reflecting faithfully improvement, lack of change, and worsening in the condition of the patient. Other applications, not yet reported in detail, have produced equally promising results both with the test battery described in this report and with other simple psychomotor measurements. It will be recalled that the tests reported here served only as samples of fine psychomotor activity, and although they seem to provide hopeful and convenient measures, many other types of psychomotor performance must also be sampled and investigated. Our need for improved theory and practical methods in the study of the behavior disorders remains urgent, and the psychomotor approach to the investigation of mental disease gives every indication of offering rewarding study.

CHAPTER 10

SUMMARY AND CONCLUSIONS

In Part I of this report it was stated that few, if any, physical, physiologic, or psychologic test methods have been found to be effective in the definition of mental disease or have served to extend significantly the clinical opinion formed on the basis of knowledge of the behavior of a patient and of his life history. We have so imperfect a grasp of the mechanisms of mental disorder, beyond the level of symptom expression, that we have been unable to bring physical, physiologic, or psychologic methods to bear upon the problem fruitfully. Some of the reasons for this inability to outline the basic mechanisms of mental disease may be better appreciated if it is realized that, over and beyond the problem presented by diseased and disordered mental function, we are at grips with the old and difficult problem of the relation of mind to brain, or mind and body. Some light may be shed on this historic problem by study of the mind in disorder, or by the experimental manipulation of structural and functional neurologic control of behavior; both methods are being applied in this laboratory. The present report is concerned with observations upon the psychomotor functioning of individuals suffering from a behavior disorder. It became apparent, in the course of study of the effects upon psychologic function of removal of frontal cortical tissue from the human brain, that disturbances of psychomotor function could be demonstrated systematically in chronic mental patients if sufficiently sensitive test methods and procedures were employed. It seemed, further, that the degree of psychomotor disturbance was related to the clinical estimate of the extent of disorder present in behavior, and that the defects in psychomotor performance were increased quantitatively immediately following the removal of frontal brain gray matter.

The present experiment was undertaken to test more thoroughly the existence of a possible relation between psychomotor function and behavior disorder, and to examine in greater detail any positive trends which might emerge. The test methods selected for experimental use center upon fine psychomotor movement, or those movements made with the smaller musculatures rather than a total bodily involvement. The experimental battery was made up of tests which seemed to represent most adequately the principal components of fine psychomotor ability as these emerged from a factor analysis of performance on a number of fine psychomotor tests. These sample tests are singularly free of influence by extraneous factors —e.g., intelligence, practical experience, the socio-economic background of the subject, etc.—are simple to grasp, and may be repeated many times over without being exhaustive in time or effort. They possess a common factor of speed of mobilization and appear to be basic in the sense of indivisibility. The battery consists of tests of *reaction time* as a measure of the speed of initiating movement, *speed of tapping* as a measure of speed in stereotyped wrist-arm movement, and *finger dexterity* as a measure of speed in finger and manual dexterity and precision. To these basic tasks have been added tests of disjunctive reaction time to serve as supplementary measures of elementary discriminative response. It has been stressed that the tests employed were selected as promising sample measures of a particular type of activity chosen for a specific use, and do not presume to represent the only important measures of psychomotor function. This battery of tests, which includes measures of the speed of initiating, continuing, and controlling fine psychomotor movements, was individually administered to a group of normal subjects, a group of chronic schizophrenic patients with varying degrees of behavior disorder, and groups of patients with diagnoses of pseudoneurotic schizophrenia and psychoneurosis. Practice and familiarity with the psychomotor tasks are required to achieve stability in response, and the notation of the course of learning during such practice has provided measures of the psychomotor learning function in each of the groups studied.

Part II lists the findings when the test battery was applied to the various experimental groups:

1. Base-line standards of average performance and variability of response were established for a group of 194 normal subjects on each test of the experimental battery. This sample, including subjects of both sexes, covered an age range of 20–70 years, with an average age of 42.2 years.

2. Learning curves for performance on each of the tasks exhibited regular processes of acquisition, reaching a stable level of response within the period of observation. The dexterity measures presented an exception.

3. An age factor was clearly manifested; a sex factor was also present but minimal. Age must be considered in comparing those experimental groups which differ in average age, but sex may be disregarded in the comparison of groups similarly composed.

4. The three essential performance factors under investigation were seen to be only partially intercorrelated, though performance on different tasks relating to the same factor was clearly related.

5. These data were in agreement with normative data reported by other investigators using similar apparatus and procedures. They should serve as a satisfactory basis for the comparison of performance by psychopathologic groups.

6. The practice learning curves of performance by the chronic schizophrenic group (90 patients) were found to be regular and to be similar, if not identical, to those observed in repeated performance by normal subjects.

7. A comparison of performance by the chronic schizophrenes and normal subjects revealed distinct retardation in average performance by the schizophrenes on all tests. Variability was markedly increased in the schizophrenic group on tasks of initiating single responses, but was of a similar order to that of the normal group on all other tests.

8. The ratio of simple to disjunctive reaction time was essentially the same as that observed for the normal group. The pattern of interrelation in performance on the several tests was found to be similar to that of the normal group and somewhat intensified.

9. Gradation of patients within the chronic schizophrenic group, in terms of the degree of expression of behavior disorder, whether made on the basis of psychiatric or psychologic behavior rating scales, hospital management criteria, duration of illness, or psycho-

pathologic type, was accompanied by a shading off of performance scores on all psychomotor tasks, indicating a close correspondence between performance on the test battery and clinical status.

10. An analysis of the chronic schizophrenic group on the variables of sex, age, education, and body type failed to indicate significant trends in terms of either clinical status or psychomotor performance.

11. The practice learning curves of performance by the subacute group (neurotic and pseudoneurotic schizophrenic groups combined, totaling 50) on each task exhibited a close similarity to those produced by the normal group.

12. A comparison of performance by the subacute group and normal subjects indicated that, although the performance of the subacute group was more like that of the normal than was that of chronic schizophrenes, this group was also consistently retarded in fine psychomotor performance. This trend in mean scores was accompanied by a tendency toward expanded variability on tasks of initiating single responses, whereas variation on other tasks was of a similar order to that of the normal group.

13. The ratio of simple to disjunctive reaction time was essentially the same as that observed with normal subjects. The matrix of interrelation of performance among the several tasks was also very similar to that obtained from normal subjects.

14. Gradation of patients within the subacute group, by classifying the subjects diagnostically as neurotic or pseudoneurotic schizophrenic, revealed that most of the deviation from normal observed for the subacute group may be attributed to those subjects falling in the pseudoneurotic schizophrenic group.

In Part III the principal finding of a clear defect in psychomotor performance which characterized states of disordered behavior was discussed. The defect was found to be of varying degree and positively related to the type and amount of behavior deviation present. When a division of the subacute behavior disorders was made into psychoneurotic and pseudoneurotic schizophrenic subjects, the pseudoneurotic schizophrenics showed a pattern of defect similar to that described by chronic schizophrenes but in an attenuated form, while performance by the psychoneurotic subjects more closely resembled that of the normal subjects. The psychomotor retardation observed thus seemed to be related to the schizophrenic disorder. To extend the meaningfulness of these findings and to attempt to develop a better grasp of the relations existing between psychomotor performance and behavior disorder generally, a survey was made of the experiments of other investigators who have, directly or indirectly, produced data relevant to this relationship. From this review has emerged a general pattern of faulty performance on a wide variety of psychomotor tasks by individuals suffering from mental disease, which is particularly striking among schizophrenic subjects. The pervasive nature of this effect suggests the operation of broad factors. Two hypotheses to account for the data observed have been advanced:

1. That the observed faulty psychomotor performance of subjects with a behavior disorder is a secondary, symptomatic reflection of a general blunting of performance and participation by the patient, in terms of mental disorganization and attitudinal factors, e.g., withdrawal, negativism, preoccupation, etc.

2. That the observed faulty psychomotor performance of subjects with a behavior disorder is a primary indication of disturbance in a basic adaptational process, that of motor adjustment to the external surround.

Details of the data from this experiment did not fully support the first hypothesis: a comparison of psychomotor and other psychologic test performance requiring patience, fine discrimination, and persistence showed a relatively much greater defect in tasks of the psychomotor type; acquisition functions were found to be much the same for individuals with a behavior disorder as for normal subjects; the matrix of intercorrelations among tasks of the experimental battery did not reflect the entry of a strong ordering factor, etc. To evaluate properly the second hypothesis required some reformulation of the role of psychomotor activity in animate existence. It was stated that the power of movement and the adjustment to the surround by motion is a fundamental capacity of animate life. The hypothesis was developed that despite the confusing overlay of increased complexity of stimulus reception and response capacity in human life, the movement capacity remains a basic adaptive mechanism. In mental disease, and in schizophrenia in particular, there is a central failure of adaptation which includes, in a basic sense, the psychomotor. Further specifically designed experiments will be required to test this hypothesis adequately, but the present observations would make it appear that a fundamental disturbance of psychomotor function does indeed occur systematically in the behavior disorders.

Several general points of view have been brought forward:

1. That psychomotility is conceived as a broad range of human activity deserving of study as a fundamental psychologic component and primary adaptive characteristic of life.

2. That the basic adaptation achieved by means of the motor system in animals is one of the essential life processes, the greater control of which gives rise to mentation in animals and mind in man.

3. That the psychomotor capacity appears to be disturbed in a fundamental sense in the behavior disorders. As such, it is a reflection of defect at the core, rather than in the periphery, of mind and mental process. Those suffering from mental disease are, by definition as well as current theory, persons who demonstrate a faulty adaptation to their environment. Retarded and faulty psychomotor response is regarded as a basic indication of this state of psychobiologic maladaptation.

Bibliography

BIBLIOGRAPHY

1. Albino, R. C. The stable and labile personality types of Luria in clinically normal individuals. *Brit. J. Psychol.*, 1948, *39*, 54–60.
2. Allport, G. W., and Vernon, P. E. *Studies in expressive movement.* New York: Macmillan, 1933.
3. Alprin, S. Relationship of pursuit rotor performance to self adjustment. *Mot. Skills Res. Exch.*, 1950, *2*, 16.
4. Alprin, S. The relationship of self adjustment to pursuit rotor performance. *Mot. Skills Res. Exch.*, 1950, *2*, 36–39.
5. Arps, W. Uber der motorische Leistungsfähigkeit bei Grundschulkindern der Spracheil-, Volks- und Hilfsschule. *Hamburg. Lehrztg.*, 1934, *13*, 597–599.
6. Ascher, E. Motor attitudes and psychotherapy. *Psychosom. Med.*, 1949, *11*, 228–234.
7. Barnacle, C. H., Ebaugh, F. G., and Lemere, F. Association-motor investigation of the psychoneuroses. *Amer. J. Psychiat.*, 1935, *91*, 925–937.
8. Bell, J. E. *Projective techniques.* New York: Longmans, Green, 1948.
9. Bender, L. A visual motor Gestalt test and its clinical use. *Amer. Orthopsychiat. Assoc., Res. Monogr. 3,* 1938, 1–176.
10. Berrien, F. K. Finger oscillations as indices of emotion. I. Preliminary validation. *J. exp. Psychol.*, 1939, *24*, 485–498.
11. Berrien, F. K. Finger oscillations as indices of emotion. II. Further validation and use in detecting deception. *J. exp. Psychol.*, 1939, *24*, 609–620.
12. Billingslea, F. The Bender-Gestalt test: An objective scoring method and validating data. *J. clin. Psychol.*, 1948, *4*, 1–28.
13. Bingham, W. V. *Mot. Skills Res. Exch.* 1950, *2*, 2.
14. Bleuler, E. *Dementia Praecox.* New York: International Univ. Press, 1950.
15. Brace, D. K. Motor learning of feebleminded girls. *Res. Quart. Amer. Ass. Hlth.*, 1948, *19*, 269–275.
16. Brower, D., and Oppenheim, S. The effects of electroshock therapy on mental functions as revealed by psychological tests. *J. gen. Psychol.*, 1951, *45*, 171–188.
17. Brunner, W. Charakterfestellung durch Bewegungsproben. *Industr. Psychotech.*, 1934, *11*, 361–371.
18. Burtt, H. E. Motor concomitants of the association reaction. *J. exp. Psychol.*, 1936, *19*, 51–63.
19. Canestrelli, L. Aspetti della personalita rivelati dai processi di adattamento psicomotorio. Analisi psicologica di un atto reattivo volontario con l'aiuto del metodo fotociclografico. *Arch. Psicol. Neurol. Psichiat.*, 1941, *2*, 272–379.
20. Chorus, A. M. J. Les enfants instables; psychomoteurs purs. *Z. Kinderpsychiat.*, 1942, *8*, 161–173.

21. Chorus, A. M. J. Le rythme personnel (das persönliche Tempo) et le rythme de travail des enfants instables. *Z. Kinderpsychiat.*, 1943, *10*, 2–8.
22. Chorus, A. M. J. Le rythme personnel (das persönliche Tempo) et le rythme de travail des enfants instables. *Z. Kinderpsychiat.*, 1943, *10*, 40–51.
23. Clausen, J. Respiration movement in normal, neurotic and psychotic subjects. *Acta psychiat., Kbh.*, 1951, Suppl. *68*, 1–74.
24. Coghill, G. E. *Anatomy and the problem of behaviour.* London: Cambridge Univ. Press, 1929.
25. Cohen, L. H., Malmo, R. B., and Thale, T. Measurements of chronic psychotic overactivity by the Norwich Rating Scale. *J. gen. Psychol.*, 1944, *30*, 65–74.
26. Columbia Greystone Associates. *Selective partial ablation of the frontal cortex.* New York: Hoeber, 1949.
27. Columbia Greystone Associates (second group). *Psychosurgical problems.* Philadelphia: Blakiston, 1952.
28. Columbia Greystone Associates. *Psychosurgical problems.* Vol. II. *J. nerv. ment. Dis. Monogr.* (in press).
29. Committee on Nomenclature and Statistics of the American Psychiatric Association. *Mental disorders: diagnostic and statistical manual.* Washington, D.C.: APA Mental Hospital Service, 1952.
30. Cook, W. E. Letter printing and anxiety. *Mot. Skills Res. Exch.*, 1952, *4*, 44.
31. Cross, H. M. The motor capacities of stutterers. *Arch. Speech.*, 1936, *1*, 112–132.
32. Davis, D. R. Disorders of skill: an experimental approach to some problems of neurosis. *Mot. Skills. Res. Exch.*, 1950, *2*, 56.
33. De Montmollin, M. Les tests moteurs. I. *Rev. Psychol. appl.*, 1951, *1*, 29–49. Les tests moteurs. II. *Rev. Psychol. appl.*, 1951, *1*, 85–92. Les tests moteurs. III. *Rev. Psychol. appl.*, 1951, *1*, 227–230.
34. Drew, G. C. Variations in reflex blink-rate during visual-motor tasks. *Quart. J. exp. Psychol.*, 1951, *3*, 73–88.
35. Filippini, A. Adattamento ed apprendimento di lavori manuali quale segno della personalità. *Arch. Psicol. Neurol. Psichiat.*, 1941, *2*, 380–390.
36. Fulton, J. F. *A textbook of physiology.* 16th Ed. Philadelphia: Saunders, 1949.
37. Gardner, J. W. An experimental study of the Luria technique for detecting mental conflict. *J. exp. Psychol.*, 1936, *19*, 495–506.
38. Garrett, H. E. Variability in learning under massed and spaced practice. *J. exp. Psychol.*, 1940, *26*, 547–567.
39. Garrett, H. E. *Great experiments in psychology.* New York: Appleton-Century, 1941.
40. Garrison, M. Affectivity. In *Selective partial ablation of the frontal cortex.* Columbia Greystone Associates, New York: Hoeber, 1949.
41. Glanville, A. D., and Kreezer, G. Deficiencies in amplitude of joint movement associated with mental deficiency. *Child Developm.*, 1937, *8*, 129–138.
42. Goodenough, F. L., and Harris, D. B. Studies in the psychology of children's drawings: II, 1928–1949. *Psychol. Bull.*, 1950, *47*, 369–433.
43. Harrison, R., and Dorcus, R. M. Is rate of voluntary movement unitary? *J. gen. Psychol.*, 1938, *18*, 31–39.
44. Heath, R. G. *Selective partial ablation of the frontal cortex.* Columbia Greystone Associates. New York: Hoeber, 1949, p. 410.
45. Heath, S. R., Jr. Rail-walking performance as related to mental age and etiological type among the mentally retarded. *Amer. J. Psychol.*, 1942, *55*, 240–247.
46. Herrick, C. J. *Brains of rats and men.* Chicago: Univ. of Chicago Press, 1926.

47. Hoch, P., and Polatin, P. Pseudoneurotic forms of schizophrenia. *Psychiat. Quart.*, 1949, *23*, 248–276.
48. Hunt, J. M., and Cofer, C. N. Psychological deficit. In *Personality and the behavior disorders* (Ed., J. M. Hunt). New York: Ronald, 1944.
49. Huston, P. E. Eye-hand coordination in schizophrenic patients and normals as measured by the pursuit meter. *Psychol. Bull.*, 1932, *29*, 662.
50. Huston, P. E., and Shakow, D. Studies of motor function in schizophrenia: III. Steadiness. *J. gen. Psychol.*, 1946, *34*, 119–126.
51. Huston, P. E., Shakow, D., and Erickson, M. H. A study of hypnotically induced complexes by means of the Luria technique. *J. gen. Psychol.*, 1934, *11*, 65–97.
52. Huston, P. E., Shakow, D., and Riggs, L. A. Studies of motor function in schizophrenia: II. Reaction time. *J. gen. Psychol.*, 1937, *16*, 39–82.
53. Jampolsky, P. Une nouvelle épreuve psychomotrice; premiers résultats génétiques et cliniques. *Rev. Psychol. appl.*, 1951, *1*, 103–138.
54. Jones, M. R. Measurements of spontaneous movements in adult psychotic patients by a time-sampling technique: a methodological study. *J. Psychol.*, 1941, *11*, 285–295.
55. Jones, M. R. Studies in "nervous" movements: I. The effect of mental arithmetic on the frequency and patterning of movements. *J. gen. Psychol.*, 1943, *29*, 47–62.
56. Jones, M. R. Studies in "nervous" movements: II. The effect of inhibition of micturition on the frequency and patterning of movements. *J. gen. Psychol.*, 1943, *29*, 303–312.
57. Kallmann, F. J. *The genetics of schizophrenia.* New York: Augustine, 1938.
58. Kallmann, F. J. The genetic theory of schizophrenia: an analysis of 691 schizophrenic twin index families. *Amer. J. Psychiat.*, 1946, *103*, 309–322.
59. Kinder, E., and Humphreys, E. The observation room as a method for the investigation of the behavior of mental defectives. *Proc. Amer. Ass. ment. Def.*, 1936, *41*, 71–81.
60. Kinder, E., *et al.* Time sampling study of behavior. In *Psychosurgical problems.* Vol. I. Columbia Greystone Associates (2nd Group). Philadelphia: Blakiston, 1952.
61. Kinder, E., *et al.* Time sampling study of behavior. In *Psychosurgical problems.* Vol. II. Columbia Greystone Associates (2nd Group). *J. nerv. ment. Dis. Monogr.* (in press).
62. King, H. E. Psychomotor aspects of the orbitofrontal cortex. *Fed. Proc.*, 1950, *9*, 70.
63. King, H. E. Intellectual function. In *Selective partial ablation of the frontal cortex,* Columbia Greystone Associates. New York: Hoeber, 1949.
64. King, H. E. Psychomotor performance and psychiatric status. *Bull. Tulane med. Faculty,* 1951, *11*, 34–37.
65. King, H. E., and Clausen, J. Simple reaction time. *Methods in medical research.* Vol. 3, 166–168. Chicago: Year Book Publ., 1950
66. King, H. E., and Clausen, J. Speed of tapping. *Methods in medical research.* Vol. 3, 175–177. Chicago: Year Book Publ., 1950.
67. King, H. E., and Clausen, J. Finger dexterity. *Methods in medical research.* Vol. 3, 193–194. Chicago: Year Book Publ., 1950.
68. King, H. E., and Clausen, J. Psychophysiology. In *Psychosurgical problems.* Vol. I. Columbia Greystone Associates (2nd Group). Philadelphia: Blakiston, 1952.
69. King, H. E., and Clausen, J. Psychophysiology. In *Psychosurgical problems.* Vol. II. Columbia Greystone Associates (2nd Group). *J. nerv. ment. Dis. Monogr.* (in press).

70. KING, H. E., *et al.* Psychologic observations. In *Studies in schizophrenia* (Ed., R. G. Heath). Cambridge: Harvard Univ. Press (in press).

71. KOPP, H. The relationship of stuttering to motor disturbances. *Nerv. Child,* 1943, *2,* 107–116.

72. KRAEPELIN, E. Der Psychologische Versuch in der Psychiatrie. *Psychol. Arb.,* 1896, *1,* 63–65.

73. KRAEPELIN, E. *Dementia Praecox and Paraphrenia* (Trans., R. M. Barclay). Edinburgh: Livingstone, 1919.

74. KRAEPELIN, E. Arbeitspsychologische Ausblicke. *Psychol. Arb.,* 1925, *8,* 431–450.

75. KRAUSE, L. S. Relation of voluntary motor pressure disorganization (Luria) to two other alleged complex indicators. *J. exp. Psychol.,* 1937, *21,* 653–661.

76. KREEZER, G. Motor studies of the mentally deficient; quantitative methods at various levels of integration. *Proc. Amer. Ass. ment. Def.,* 1935, *40,* 357–366.

77. LANDIS, C., and BOLLES, M. M. *Textbook of abnormal psychology.* Revised Edition. New York: Macmillan, 1950.

78. LANDIS, C., and ERLICK, D. An analysis of the Porteus Maze-Test as affected by psychosurgery. *Amer. J. Psychol.,* 1950, *63,* 557–566.

79. LANDIS, C., and PAGE, J. D. *Modern society and mental disease.* New York: Rinehart, 1938, p. 34.

80. LAZARUS, R. S., DEESE, J., and OSLER, S. F. The effects of psychological stress upon performance. *Psychol. Bull.,* 1952, *49,* 293–317.

81. LORD, E., and WOOD, D. Diagnostic values in a visuo-motor test. *Amer. J. Orthopsychiat.,* 1942, *12,* 414–428.

82. LUCERO, R. J., and MEYER, B. T. A behavior rating scale suitable for use in mental hospitals. *J. clin. Psychol.,* 1951, *7,* 250–254.

83. LURIA, A. R. *The nature of human conflicts* (Trans., W. H. Gantt). New York: Liveright, 1932.

84. MAILLOUX, N. M., and NEWBURGER, M. The work curves of psychotic individuals. *J. abnorm. soc. Psychol.,* 1941, *36,* 110–114.

85. MALAMUD, W., and SANDS, S. L. A revision of the psychiatric rating scale. *Amer. J. Psychiat.,* 1947, *104,* 231–237.

86. MALMO, R. B., and ANDREWS, H. L. A recording device for foot-tapping, with results from polyneuropathic subjects. *Amer. J. Psychol.,* 1945, *58,* 247–252.

87. MALMO, R. B., and SHAGASS, C. Physiologic studies of reaction to stress in anxiety and early schizophrenia. *Psychosom. Med.,* 1949, *11,* 9–24.

88. MALMO, R. B., SHAGASS, C., and DAVIS, J. F. A method for the investigation of somatic response mechanisms in psychoneurosis. *Science,* 1950, *112,* 325–329.

89. MALMO, R. B., SHAGASS, C., DAVIS, J. F., CLEGHORN, R. A., GRAHAM, B. F., and GOODMAN, A. J. Standardized pain stimulation as controlled stress in physiological studies of psychoneurosis. *Science,* 1948, *108,* 509–511.

90. MALMO, R. B., SHAGASS, C., BELANGER, D. J., and SMITH, A. A. Motor control in psychiatric patients under experimental stress. *J. abnorm. soc. Psychol.,* 1951, *46,* 539–547.

91. MCFARLAND, R. A., and BARACH, A. L. The response of psychoneurotics to variations in oxygen tension. *Amer. J. Psychiat.,* 1937, *93,* 1315–1341.

92. MEYERSON, P. G., and LANDAU, D. Tapping rhythms in neuropsychiatric patients. *J. nerv. ment. Dis.,* 1950, *63,* 351.

93. MILES, W. R. *et al.* Selected psychomotor measurement methods. In *Methods in medical research.* Vol. 3 (Ed., R. W. Gerard). Chicago: Year Book Publ., 1950.

94. MIRA Y LÓPEZ, E. Resultados del psicodiagnóstico miokinético en adolescentes normales. In Mouchet, E., *Temas actuales de psicologia normal y patológica.* Buenos Aires: Editorial Médico-Quirúrgica, 1945.

95. MITTELMANN, B. Psychodynamics of motility: Studies of adults, children and infants. Paper read before The American Psychoanalytic Association, 1952 annual meeting, Atlantic City, New Jersey.
96. MONROE, R. R. Psychiatric observations. In *Studies in schizophrenia* (Ed., R. G. Heath). Cambridge: Harvard Univ. Press (in press).
97. NANCKEN, K. Beiträge zur Persönlichkeitsforschung auf Grund einer feinmotorischen Tätigkeit. *Untersuch. Psychol. Phil.*, 1939, *14*, p. 39.
98. OBERSTEINER, H. Uber eine neue einfache Methode zur Bestimmung der psychischen Leistungsfähigkeit des Gehirnes Geisteskranker. *Virchows Arch.*, 1874, *59*, 427–458.
99. PACAUD, S. Contribution à l'étude des mouvements volontaires. *Année psychol.*, 1942, *40*, 152–170.
100. PAGE, J. D. An experimental study of the day and night motility of normal and psychotic individuals. *Arch. Psychol., N.Y.*, 1935, No. 192.
101. PASCAL, G., and SUTTELL, B. *The Bender-Gestalt Test*. New York: Grune and Stratton, 1951.
102. PATZÁY-LIEBERMANN, L. Bewegungsuntersuchungen bei Stotteren. *Zsch. f. Kinderforsch.* 1933–4, *42*, 365–368.
103. PETERS, H. N. The mirror tracing test as a measure of social maladaptation. *J. abnorm. soc. Psychol.*, 1946, *41*, 437–448.
104. PETERS, H. N., and JONES, F. D. Evaluation of group psychotherapy by means of performance tests. *J. consult. Psychol.*, 1951, *15*, 363–367.
105. PORTEUS, S. D. *The Porteus maze test and intelligence*. Palo Alto: Pacific Books, 1950.
106. PORTEUS, S. D. A survey of recent results obtained with the Porteus Maze Test. *Brit. J. educ. Psychol.*, 1952, *22*, 180–188.
107. PORTEUS, S. D., and PETERS, H. Maze test validation and psychosurgery. *Genet. Psychol. Monogr.*, 1947, *36*, 3–86.
108. RAPAPORT, D. *Diagnostic psychological testing*. Vol. I. Chicago: Year Book Publ., 1946.
109. REAM, M. J. The tapping test: A measure of motility. *Psychol. Monogr.*, 1922, No. 1, 1–31.
110. REED, J. D. Spontaneous activity of animals. *Psychol. Bull.*, 1947, *44*, 393–412.
111. RETHLINGSHAFER, D. Measurement of a motor set. *J. exp. Psychol.*, 1943, *32*, 75–81.
112. RODNICK, E. H., and SHAKOW, D. Set in the schizophrenic as measured by a composite reaction time index. *Amer. J. Psychiat.*, 1940, *97*, 214–225.
113. ROWELL, J. T. An objective method of evaluating mental status. *J. clin. Psychol.*, 1951, *7*, 255–259.
114. RUNKEL, J. E. Luria's motor method and word association in the study of deception. *J. gen. Psychol.*, 1936, *15*, 23–37.
115. SAUNDERS, E. B., and ISAACS, S. Tests of reaction time and motor inhibition in the psychoses. *Amer. J. Psychiat.*, 1929, *9*, 79–112.
116. SEASHORE, H. G. The relation of fine and gross motor abilities. *Psychol. Bull.*, 1941, *38*, 608–609.
117. SEASHORE, H. G. Some relationships of fine and gross motor abilities. *Res. Quart. Amer. Ass. Hlth. Phys. Educ.*, 1942, *13*, 259–274.
118. SEASHORE, R. H. Work and motor performance. In *Handbook of experimental psychology* (Ed., S. S. Stevens). New York: John Wiley, 1951, pp. 1341–1362.
119. SEASHORE, R. H., BUXTON, C. E., and MCCULLOM, I. N. Multiple factorial analysis of fine motor skills. *Amer. J. Psychol.*, 1940, *53*, 251–259.
120. SEASHORE, R. H., DUDEK, F. J., and HOLTZMAN, W. A factorial analysis of arm-hand precision tests. *J. appl. Psychol.*, 1949, *33*, 579–584.

121. SEASHORE, R. H., and MCCULLOM, I. N. An experimental analysis of motility as a basic motor capacity. *Psychol. Bull.,* 1934, *31,* 591–592.
122. SHAKOW, D. A study of certain aspects of motor coordination in schizophrenia with the prod meter. *Psychol. Bull.,* 1932, *29,* 661.
123. SHAKOW, D., and HUSTON, P. E. Studies of motor function in schizophrenia: I. Speed of tapping. *J. gen. Psychol.,* 1936, *15,* 63–108.
124. SHEER, D. E., and SHUTTLEWORTH, M. Psychometric Studies. In *Psychosurgical problems.* Vol. I. Columbia Greystone Associates (2nd Group). Philadelphia: Blakiston, 1952.
125. SHEER, D. E. Psychometric studies. In *Psychosurgical problems.* Vol. II. Columbia Greystone Associates (2nd Group). *J. nerv. ment. Dis. Monogr.* (in press).
126. SHERRINGTON, C. *Man on his nature.* London: Cambridge Univ. Press, 1946.
127. SIMON, J. L. The myokinetic psychodiagnosis of Dr. Emilio Mira. *Amer. J. Psychiat.,* 1943, *100,* 334–341.
128. SPERRY, R. W. Neurology and the mind-brain problem. *Amer. Scientist,* 1952, *40,* 291–312.
129. STERN, E. Sprache, Sprachstörungen, Intelligenz und Motorik. *Pract. oto-rhino-laryng.,* 1939, *2,* 212–231.
130. STRAUS, A., and LEHTINEN, L. *Psychopathology and education of the brain injured child.* New York: Grune and Stratton, 1947.
131. TATARENKO, N. P. K probleme regulyatsii motoriki u schizofrenikov. *Trud. Tsentral. psikonevrol. Inst.,* 1937, *8,* 182–189.
132. TELFORD, C. E., and STORLIE, A. The relation of respiration and reflex winking rates to muscular tension during motor learning. *J. exp. Psychol.,* 1946, *36,* 512–517.
133. TIFFIN, J., and ASHER, E. J. The Purdue pegboard: Norms and studies of reliability and validity. *J. appl. Psychol.,* 1948, *32,* 234–247.
134. TOWNSEND, E. A. A study of copying ability in children. *Genet. Psychol. Monogr.,* 1951, *43,* 3–51.
135. TUFTS COLLEGE INSTITUTE OF APPLIED EXPERIMENTAL PSYCHOLOGY. *Handbook of human engineering data.* Second edition, Special Devices Center, Office of Naval Research, 1951, Part VI.
136. WALDFOGEL, S., FINESINGER, J. E., and VERZEANO, M. The effect of low oxygen on psychologic performance tests in psychoneurotic patients and normal controls. *Psychosom. Med.,* 1950, *12,* 244–249.
137. WELLS, F. L., and KELLEY, C. M. The simple reaction in psychosis. *Amer. J. Psychiat.,* 1922, *2,* 53–59.
138. WERNER, H. Development of visuo-motor performance on the marble-board test in mentally retarded children. *J. genet. Psychol.,* 1944, *64,* 269–279.
139. WESTPHAL, G. An experimental study of certain motor abilities of stutterers. *Child Developm.,* 1933, *4,* 214–221.
140. WOODWORTH, R. *Experimental psychology.* New York: Henry Holt, 1938.
141. WULFECK, W. H. Motor function in the mentally disordered: I. A comparative investigation of motor function in psychotics, psychoneurotics and normals. *Psychol. Rec.,* 1941, *4,* 271–323.
142. WULFECK, W. H. Motor function in the mentally disordered: II. The relation of muscle tension to the performance of motor tasks. *Psychol. Rec.,* 1941, *4,* 326–348.

APPENDIX A

Clinical History Forms

CLINICAL HISTORY FORMS

The forms reproduced here indicate the guide to historical information employed in collecting related data on subjects with a behavior disorder.

1. FOR HOSPITALIZED PATIENTS

Name:.. Date:................................ No...........
Date born:.................................... Sex: M F Lateral: R L Race: W N Y
I.Q. ..../............................. Marital status: S M D W Sp Religion: P C J N
................/............................. Education (yrs)..
Occupation: ....

General physical condition:
state of health...
prominent diseases, past...
prominent diseases, present...
height............................ weight............................ blood pressure..............................
body type: pyknic asthenic athletic dysplastic
pareses, paralyses, or spasticities...
....
gait ....
EEG ....
....

Present diagnosis:..
first symptoms noted (date & type)...
date first psychiatric care...
date first hospitalization...
admitted..
....
....
....
discharged..
....
....
....
comment (quality of remission)..
....

Present hospital status:
disturbed ward ....
moderately disturbed ward ....
quiet ward ....
ground parole ....
working at institution:
with close supervision ....
without close supervision ....

Psychiatric picture:

a. presenting picture
situation requiring hospitalization
patient's chief complaint
voluntary, accepted, forced hospitalization

b. present illness
date onset
type first symptom
course
predominant symptomatology

c. previous illness
earlier personality deviations

d. personal history
birth, early development
childhood & adolescence
adult
predominant personality traits

e. family history
nationality
occupation
socio-economic status
psychologic climate, home
prominent disease in family
siblings

f. hospital course
ward behavior
visitor reaction
response to therapy
general cooperativeness
hospital activity

g. mental content
interpretation
specific basic material (e.g., "FBI after me," etc.)

2. FOR OUT-PATIENTS

Name:.. Date:.................................. No.............
Date born:.. Sex: M F Lateral: R L Race: W N Y
I.Q. ..../................................ Marital status: S M D W Sp Religion: P C J N
................/................................ Education (yrs).....................................
Occupation: ....

General physical condition:
state of health..
prominent diseases, past...
prominent diseases, present...
height.............................. weight.............................. blood pressure...............................
body type: pyknic asthenic athletic dysplastic
pareses, paralyses, or spasticities..
....
gait ....
EEG ....
....

Present diagnosis:...
first symptoms noted (date & type)..
....
date first psychiatric care...
date came to clinic...

Occupational status:

home, not working, idle	....	working part time	....
home, working at home	....	working full time with handicaps	....
		working full time, no handicaps	....

Psychiatric picture:

a. presenting picture
patient's chief complaint
voluntary, accepted, forced consultation

b. present illness
date onset
type first symptoms
course
predominant symptomatology

c. previous illness

d. personal history
birth, early development
childhood & adolescence
adult
predominant personality traits

e. family history
nationality
occupation
socio-economic status
psychologic climate, home
prominent disease in family
siblings

f. mental content
interpretation
specific basic material (e.g., "FBI after me," etc.)

APPENDIX B

Rating Scales

1. PSYCHIATRIC RATING SCALE

FUNCTION	6	5	4	3	2	1	BASE	LINE	1	2	3	4	5	6
Appearance	bizarre		decorative		overmeticulous		*Neat*	*Careless*	slovenly		incontinent (qualify)		smearing	
Motor activity	excited		agitated		restless		*Active*	*Quiet*	underactive		retarded		stuporous	
Responsivity	sticky		overdependent		suggestible		*Flexible*	*Rigid*	stubborn		resistive		negativistic	
Aggressiveness	destructive		combative		belligerent		*Dominating*	*Self-effacing*	self-deprecating		self-mutilative		suicidal	
Socialization	unrestrained		meddlesome		out-reaching		*Extraverted*	*Introverted*	shut-in		isolated		inaccessible	
Attention	uncontrolled scatter		markedly distractible		moderately distractible		*Alert*	*Detached*	preoccupied		disparative		completely withdrawn	
Speech	incessantly productive		push of speech		overtalkative		*Voluble*	*Terse*	undertalkative		retarded-uncommunicative		mute	
Nutrition	omniphagic		voracious		gluttonous		*Indulgent*	*Finicky*	anorexia		refusal		tube-fed	
Sexuality	sexually assaultive		sexually soliciting		sexually overactive		*Active* (*hetero-sexual*)	*Underactive* (*lat. homo.*)	homosexual-passive		homosexually soliciting		homosexually assaultive—open masturbation	
Sleep	severe insomnia		moderate insomnia		restless sleep		*Light*	*Heavy*	somnolent		lethargic		comatose	
Work	disruptive		scattered		overactive		*Eager*	*Indifferent*	disinterested		resistive		incapacitated (psychiatrically)	
Mood	exhilirated		euphoric		enthusiastic		*Optimistic*	*Pessimistic*	somber		despondent		deeply depressed	
Affect	spontaneous outbursts		explosively reactive		labile		*Demonstrative*	*Reserved*	inadequate		bland		inappropriate	
Feeling	panic		anxiety-guilt		tense-irritable		*Hypersensitive*	*Hyposensitive*	phlegmatic		dull		apathetic	
Awareness	confused		scattered disoriented		superficial		*Diffuse*	*Restricted*	depersonalization		cloudy		unconscious	
Associations	irrelevant		flight		tangential		*Circumstantial*	*Concise*	brief		impoverished		blocked	
Content	hallucinated deluded		ideas of reference		autism		*Projective*	*Introspective*	self-observing	conversions hypochondriasis		obsessions phobias		somatic delusions
Memory	confabulation		fabrication		obsessively reminiscent		*Detailed*	*Generalized*	mildly defective		severely defective		amnesia	
Thought processes	fragmented		alogical		loose		*Shallow*	*Critical*	rationalization		obsessive hair-splitting		obsessive doubt	

SCORING: Evaluations are placed on a score sheet (p. 171) in accordance with the rating made by this anchored scale.

SCORE SHEET

Patient: .... Date: .... Examiner: .... No.: ....

CATEGORY	6	5	4	3	2	1	BASE LINE	1	2	3	4	5	6	SCORE
Appearance														
Motor activity														
Responsivity														
Aggressiveness														
Socialization														
Attention														
Speech														
Nutrition														
Sexuality														
Sleep														
Work														
Mood														
Affect														
Feeling														
Awareness														
Associations														
Content														
Memory														
Thought processes														
													TOTAL	

Scores are based on the number of step units between the present rating of the behavior of a patient and his prepsychotic norm. Each item is scaled on a 12-point continuum, the smallest unit of difference being one-half. Normal is represented as the base line and deviations are measured to either side, depending upon whether the symptoms are directed internally or away from the person; see pp. 34–36 and Malamud and Sands.* A total score, weighting items equally, is derived.

*This scale is taken from W. Malamud and S. L. Sands, A revision of the psychiatric rating scale. *Amer. J. Psychiat.*, 1947, *104*, 231–237.

2. PSYCHOLOGIC RATING SCALE*

SCORING: Each item is scored from 0 to 40, depending upon the rating assigned. The values 0, 10, 20, 30 and 40 are assigned respectively to the five anchor points on the continuum for the item of behavior. In general, 0 represents the most extreme variation and 40 a normal performance. Several of the items are double-ended, however (Nos. 2, 3, 8, 9, 12), for the behavior described by these may vary from normal in the direction either of over- or underexpression. They are scored in terms of deviation from the midpoint, and this value is doubled to permit the final score to range between 0 and 40 so that it will be comparable with other items of the scale. The maximum score (normal subjects) is 480.

1. COOPERATION. An over-all estimate of the degree of difficulty experienced by the examiner in handling the patient

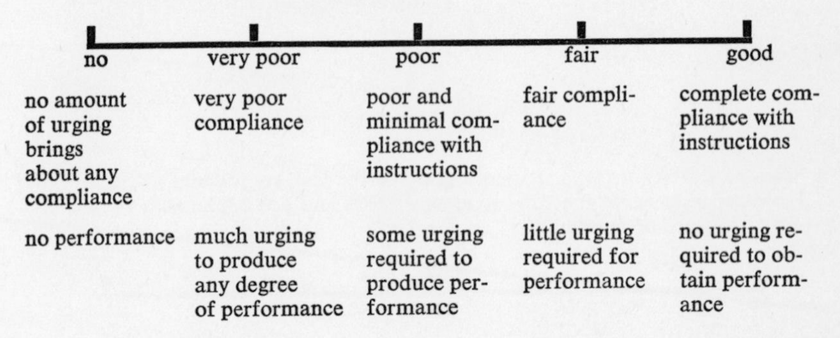

2. RELEVANT VERBALIZATION. The degree to which the patient's relevant verbalizations occur (by "relevant" is meant particularly the testing situation or other factors deemed by the examiner to be a normal topic of conversation in the interview).

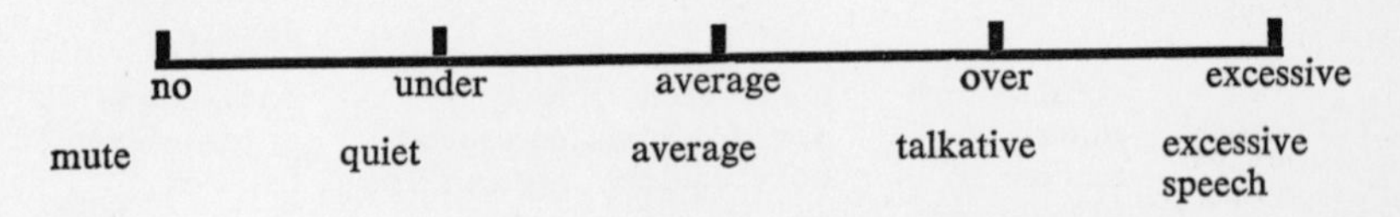

*These are selected items from the Tulane Behavior Scale (70).

3. EXPRESSIVE PLAY. An estimate of the amount of facial and bodily expression seen in the course of the interview

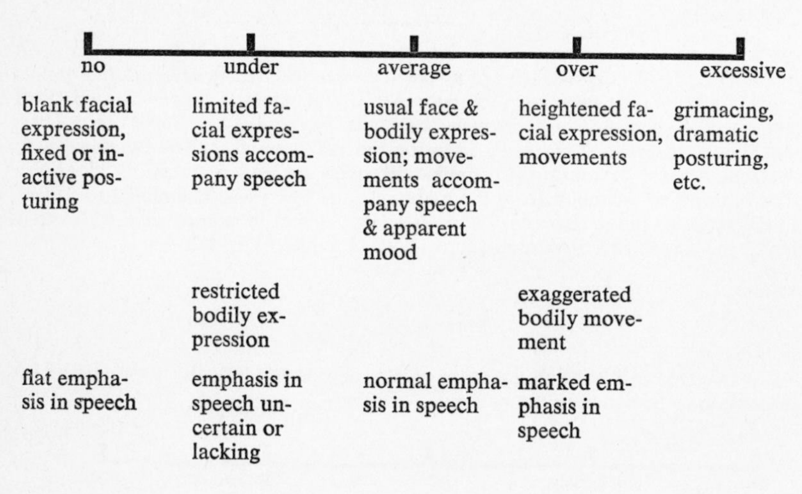

no	under	average	over	excessive
blank facial expression, fixed or inactive posturing	limited facial expressions accompany speech	usual face & bodily expression; movements accompany speech & apparent mood	heightened facial expression, movements	grimacing, dramatic posturing, etc.
	restricted bodily expression		exaggerated bodily movement	
flat emphasis in speech	emphasis in speech uncertain or lacking	normal emphasis in speech	marked emphasis in speech	

4. GRASP OF INSTRUCTIONS. Patient's grasp of the task set for him as rated by the examiner in terms of the number of repetitions and side explanations required—*not* a measure of motivation

no	very poor	poor	fair	good
complete failure to grasp task, no matter how much explanation given	much difficulty in grasp of task	difficulty in grasp of task	no particular difficulty in grasp of task	no difficulty in grasp of task
				understands quickly
	constant repetition & corrections required to produce any performance	many repetitions & corrections required	only occasional repetition or corrections required	no repetition or corrections required

5. Effort on Test. The examiner's estimate of the degree to which the patient was motivated to comply with instructions and complete the task set for him

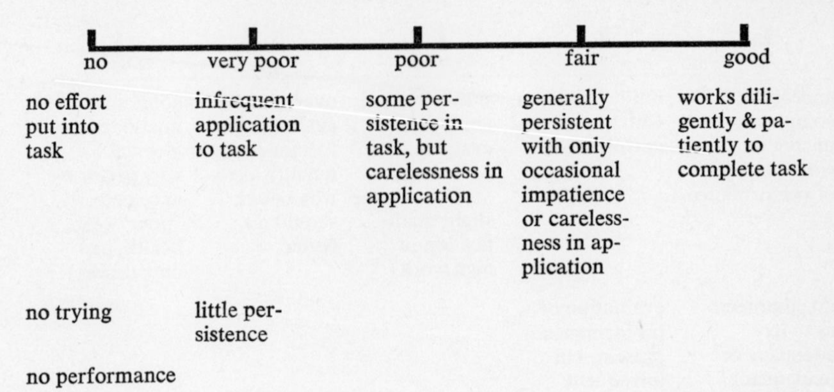

no	very poor	poor	fair	good
no effort put into task	infrequent application to task	some persistence in task, but carelessness in application	generally persistent with only occasional impatience or carelessness in application	works diligently & patiently to complete task
no trying	little persistence			
no performance				

6. Willingness. The examiner's estimate of the subject's attitude of acceptance of the task itself as an activity

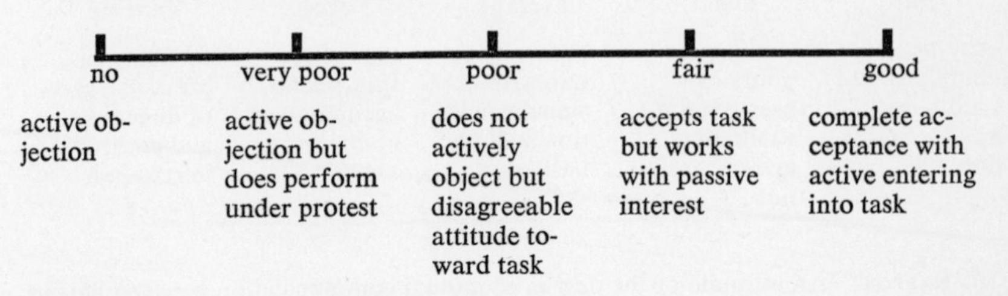

no	very poor	poor	fair	good
active objection	active objection but does perform under protest	does not actively object but disagreeable attitude toward task	accepts task but works with passive interest	complete acceptance with active entering into task
refuses to accept task				

7. Attention to Test. An estimate of the entrance of distraction into test performance (i.e., the objective nature of the task—how well can lose *self* in it)

no	very poor	poor	fair	good
completely inattentive	attention wandering	attention limited	usually attentive	complete attention given
concerned with things other than task; no performance	can fix attention for only very short periods	frequent reminding required	only occasional distractions	absorbed in task

8. Self-criticism. Estimate of the individual's ability to evaluate his own performance as indicated by speech and/or action

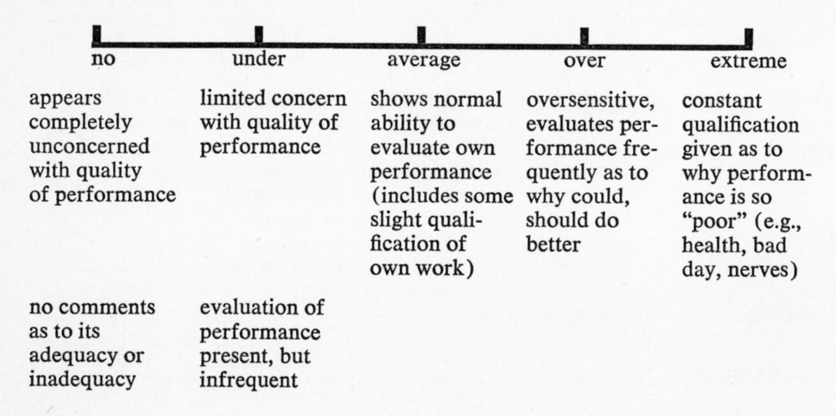

no	under	average	over	extreme
appears completely unconcerned with quality of performance	limited concern with quality of performance	shows normal ability to evaluate own performance (includes some slight qualification of own work)	oversensitive, evaluates performance frequently as to why could, should do better	constant qualification given as to why performance is so "poor" (e.g., health, bad day, nerves)
no comments as to its adequacy or inadequacy	evaluation of performance present, but infrequent			

9. Self-confidence. The degree of the individual's assertiveness as to the adequacy of his performance, by speech and/or action

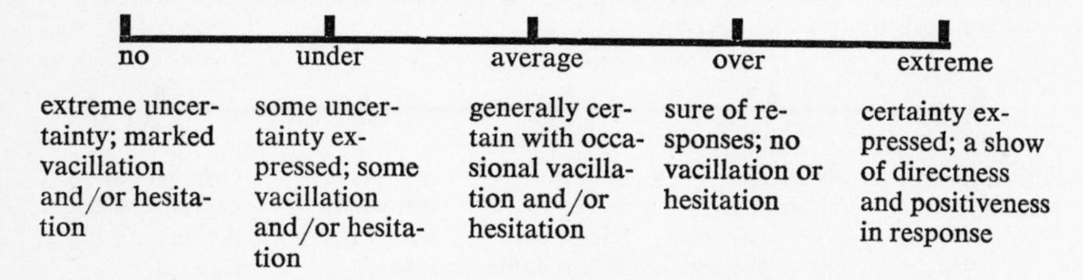

no	under	average	over	extreme
extreme uncertainty; marked vacillation and/or hesitation	some uncertainty expressed; some vacillation and/or hesitation	generally certain with occasional vacillation and/or hesitation	sure of responses; no vacillation or hesitation	certainty expressed; a show of directness and positiveness in response

10. Rapport. An estimate of the degree of mutual communication between patient and examiner, based upon contact with the examiner as immediate environment

no	very poor	poor	fair	good
no interpersonal contact at all	weak, uncertain interpersonal contact	indirect, strained interpersonal contact	direct, but reserved interpersonal contact	direct, friendly interpersonal contact
no empathy or common feeling with examiner	only infrequent accord	uncertain accord on task & general situation	some accord on tasks & general situation, but lacking in ease	easy accord on tasks & general situation
	only occasional flashes of feeling with examiner	appears not to feel with examiner	seems to feel with examiner most of time	close relation in feeling with examiner

11. Intrusion of Psychotic Influence. The examiner's estimate of psychotic coloring which becomes manifest in the course of the interview by speech and/or action (includes such factors as bizarreness, irrational speech, delusions, irrational fears, mutism, posturing, inappropriate emotion, etc.)

very strong | strong | slight | very slight | no

12. Personal Concern with the Examiner. The degree to which the patient seems concerned with the examiner as another individual and expresses either curiosity or interest in the examiner as a *person* rather than as an examiner

no	minor	mild	curious	very active
no concern whatsoever with examiner as person	only rare questions	questions as to why doing this work, examiner's position and specialty	interest in examiner's position, private life, etc.	close personal questioning on examiner's position, private life, etc., to point of preoccupying curiosity
no personal questions or curiosity	accepts as a doctor			
completely passive to examiner as "institution"				

APPENDIX C

Wiring Diagrams

1. REACTION TIME APPARATUS

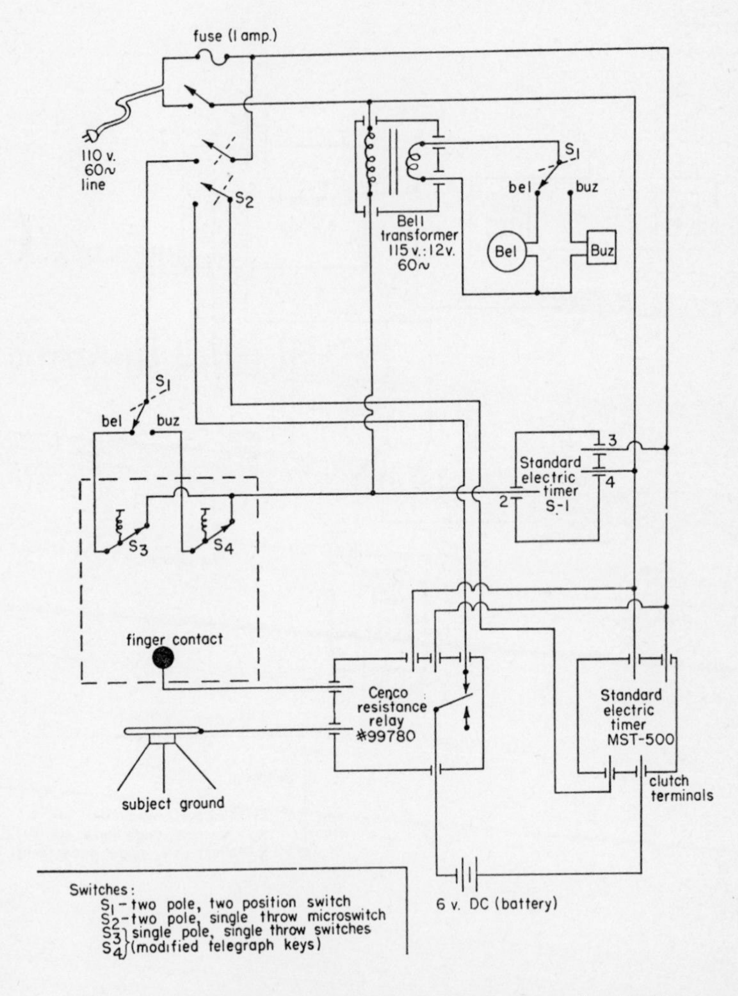

The order of stimulus presentation for *DRT* (*L*) and *DRT* (*J*):

Practice series: Z,Z,L,Z,L,Z,L,L,Z,L

Measure series: L,Z,L,L,Z,L,Z,L,Z,Z

Z = buzzer L = bell

2. TAPPING SPEED APPARATUS

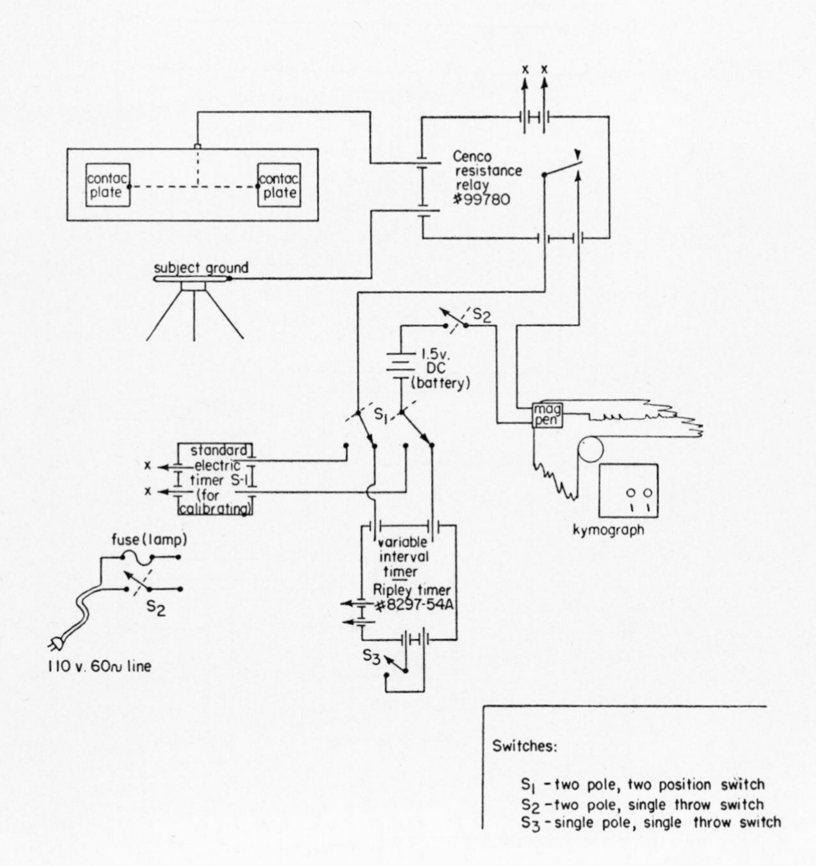

Index

SUBJECT INDEX